STUDENT MATHEMATICAL LIB
Volume 29

Matrix Groups
for Undergraduates

Kristopher Tapp

AMERICAN MATHEMATICAL SOCIETY

Editorial Board

2000 *Mathematics Subject Classification.* Primary 20-02, 20G20;
Secondary 22C05, 22E15.

The artwork on the cover is a computer-manipulated photograph created
by Charity Hendrickson and Kristopher Tapp.

For additional information and updates on this book, visit
www.ams.org/bookpages/stml-29

Library of Congress Cataloging-in-Publication Data

Tapp, Kristopher, 1971-
   Matrix groups for undergraduates / Kristopher Tapp.
      p. cm. – (Student mathematical library, ISSN 1520-9121 ; v. 29)
   Includes bibliographical references and index.
   ISBN 0-8218-3785-0 (pbk. : acid-free paper)
   1. Matrix groups. 2. Linear algebraic groups. 3. Compact groups. 4. Lie
groups. I. Title. II. Series.

QA184.2.T37   2005
512′.2–dc22   2005041182

Contents

Contents

Why study matrix groups?

A matrix group means a group of invertible matrices. This definition sounds simple enough and purely algebraic. You know from linear algebra that invertible matrices represent geometric motions (i.e., linear transformations) of vector spaces, so maybe it's not so surprising that matrix groups are useful within geometry. It turns out that matrix groups pop up in virtually any investigation of objects with symmetries, such as molecules in chemistry, particles in physics, and projective spaces in geometry. Here are some examples of how amazingly ubiquitous matrix groups have become in mathematics, physics and other fields:

- Four-dimensional topology, particle physics and Yang-Mills connections are inter-related theories based heavily on matrix groups, particularly on a certain double-cover between two matrix groups (see Section 8.7).

- Movie graphics programmers use matrix groups for rotating and translating three-dimensional objects on a computer screen (see Section 3.6).

- The theory of differential equations relies on matrix groups, particularly on matrix exponentiation (see Chapter 6).

- The shape of the universe might be a quotient of a certain matrix group, $Sp(1)$, as recently proposed by Jeff Weeks (see Section 8.6). Weeks writes, "Matrix groups model possible shapes for the universe. Conceptually one thinks of the universe as a single multi-connected space, but when cosmologists roll up their sleeves to work on such models they find it far easier to represent them as a simply connected space under the action of a matrix group."

- Quantum computing is based on the group of unitary matrices (see Section 3.2). William Wootters writes, "A quantum computation, according to one widely used model, is nothing but a sequence of unitary transformations. One starts with a small repertoire of simple unitary matrices, some 2×2 and some 4×4, and combines them to generate, with arbitrarily high precision, an approximation to any desired unitary transformation on a huge vector space."

- In a linear algebra course, you may have learned that certain types of matrices can be diagonalized or put into other nice forms. The theory of matrix groups provides a beautifully uniform way of understanding such normal forms (see Chapter 9), which are essential tools in disciplines ranging from topology and geometry to discrete math and statistics.

- Riemannian geometry relies heavily on matrix groups, in part because the isometry group of any compact Riemannian manifold is a matrix group. More generally, since the work of Klein, the word "geometry" itself is often understood as the study of invariants of the action of a matrix group on a space.

Matrix groups are used in algebraic geometry, complex analysis, group and ring theory, number theory, quantum physics, Einstein's special relativity, Heisenberg's uncertainty principle, quark theory, Fourier series, combinatorics, and many more areas; see Howe's article [**10**]. Howe writes that matrix groups "touch a tremendous spectrum of mathematical areas...the applications are astonishing in their pervasiveness and sometimes in their unexpectedness."

You will discover that matrix groups are simultaneously algebraic and geometric objects. This text will help you build bridges between your knowledge of algebra and geometry. In fact, the beautiful richness of the subject derives from the interplay between the algebraic and geometric structure of matrix groups. You'll see.

My goal is to develop rigorously and clearly the basic structures of matrix groups. This text is elementary, requires few prerequisites, and provides substantial geometric motivation. Whenever possible, my approach is concrete and driven by examples. Exploring the symmetries of a sphere is a motivating thread woven through the text, beginning with the cover artwork. You will need only the following prerequisites:

- **Calculus:** topics through multivariable calculus, with a brief introduction to complex numbers including Euler's formula

$$e^{i\theta} = \cos(\theta) + i\sin(\theta).$$

- **Linear Algebra:** determinant, trace, eigenvalues, eigenvectors, vector spaces, linear transformations and their relationship to matrices, change of basis via conjugation.

- **Abstract Algebra:** groups, normal subgroups, quotient groups, abelian groups, fields.

- **Analysis (optional):** topology of Euclidean space (open, closed, limit point, compact, connected), sequences and series, continuous and differentiable functions from $\mathbb{R}^m$ to $\mathbb{R}^n$, the inverse function theorem.

The analysis prerequisites are optional. I will develop these analysis topics from scratch for readers seeing this material for the first time, but since this is not an analysis textbook, I will not feel obliged to include complete proofs of analysis theorems.

I believe that matrix groups should become a more common staple of the undergraduate curriculum; my hope is that this text will help allow a movement in that direction.

I would like to thank Frank Morgan, Ed Burger, Tom Garrity, Phil Straffin, Wolfgang Ziller and Satyan Devadoss for sharing valuable suggestions. I am indebted to several authors of previous texts about matrix groups, particularly Curtis [**3**], Howe [**10**], Baker [**1**], Rossmann [**11**] and Hall [**7**]. I wish to thank Charity for support, love and understanding as I wrote this book. Finally, I wish to dedicate this text to Willow Jean Tapp, born March 17, 2004.

Chapter 1

Matrices

In this chapter, we define quaternionic numbers and discuss basic algebraic properties of matrices, including the correspondence between matrices and linear transformations. We begin with a visual example that motivates the topic of matrix groups.

1. Rigid motions of the sphere: a motivating example

The simplest interesting matrix group, called $SO(3)$, can be described in the following (admittedly imprecise) way:

$$SO(3) = \text{all positions of a globe on a fixed stand.}$$

Three elements of $SO(3)$ are pictured in Figure 1. Though the globe always occupies the same place in space, the three elements differ in the directions where various countries face.

Figure 1. Three elements of $SO(3)$.

Let's call the first picture "the identity". Every other element of $SO(3)$ is achieved, starting with the identity, by physically moving the globe in some way. $SO(3)$ becomes a group under composition of motions (since different motions might place the globe in the same position, think about why this group operation is well-defined). Several questions come to mind.

Question 1.1. *Is $SO(3)$ an abelian group?*

The North Pole of the globe faces up in the identity position. Rotating the globe around the axis through the North and South Pole provides a "circle's worth" of elements of $SO(3)$ for which the North Pole faces up. Similarly, there is a circle's worth of elements of $SO(3)$ for which the North Pole is located as in picture 2, or at any other point of the globe. Any element of $SO(3)$ is achieved, starting with the identity, by first moving the North Pole to the correct position and then rotating about the axis through its new position. It is therefore natural to ask:

Question 1.2. *Is there a natural bijection between $SO(3)$ and the product $S^2 \times S^1 := \{(p, \theta) \mid p \in S^2, \theta \in S^1\}$?*

Here S^2 denotes the sphere (the surface of the globe) and S^1 denotes the circle, both special cases of the general definition of an n-dimensional sphere:

$$S^n := \{(x_1, ..., x_{n+1}) \in \mathbb{R}^{n+1} \mid x_1^2 + \cdots + x_{n+1}^2 = 1\}.$$

Graphics programmers, who model objects moving and spinning in space, need an efficient way to represent the rotation of such objects. A bijection $SO(3) \cong S^2 \times S^1$ would help, allowing any rotation to be coded using only three real numbers – two which locate a point of S^2 and one angle which locates a point of S^1. If no such bijection exists, can we nevertheless understand the shape of $SO(3)$ sufficiently well to somehow parameterize its elements via three real numbers?

One is tempted to refer to elements of $SO(3)$ as "rotations" of the sphere, but perhaps there are motions more complicated than rotations.

Question 1.3. *Can every element of $SO(3)$ be achieved, starting with the identity, by rotating through some angle about some single axis?*

If so, then for any element of $SO(3)$, there must be a pair of antipodal points of the globe in their identity position.

You might borrow your roommate's basketball and use visual intuition to guess the correct answers to Questions 1.1, 1.2 and 1.3. But our definition of $SO(3)$ is probably too imprecise to lead to rigorous proofs of your answers. We will return to these questions after developing the algebraic background needed to define $SO(3)$ in a more precise way, as a group of matrices.

2. Fields and skew-fields

A matrix is an array of numbers, but what type of numbers? Matrices of real numbers and matrices of complex numbers are familiar. Are there other good choices? We need to add, multiply and invert matrices, so we must choose a number system with a notion of addition, multiplication, and division; in other words, we must choose a field or a skew-field.

Definition 1.4. *A skew-field is a set, $\mathbb{K}$, together with operations called addition (denoted "+") and multiplication (denoted "·") satisfying:*

(1) $a \cdot (b + c) = a \cdot b + a \cdot c$ *and* $(b + c) \cdot a = b \cdot a + c \cdot a$.

(2) $\mathbb{K}$ *is an abelian group under addition, with identity denoted as* "0".

(3) $\mathbb{K} - \{0\}$ *is a group under multiplication, with identity denoted as* "1".

A skew-field in which multiplication is commutative ($a \cdot b = b \cdot a$) is called a field.

The real numbers, $\mathbb{R}$, and the rational numbers, $\mathbb{Q}$, are fields. The plane $\mathbb{R}^2$ is NOT a field under the operations of component-wise addition and multiplication:

$$(a, b) + (c, d) := (a + c, b + d)$$
$$(a, b) \cdot (c, d) := (ac, bd),$$

because, for example, the element $(5, 0)$ does not have a multiplicative inverse (no element times $(5, 0)$ equals $(1, 1)$, which is the only possible identity element). A similar argument shows that for $n > 1$, $\mathbb{R}^n$ is not a field under component-wise addition and multiplication.

In order to make $\mathbb{R}^2$ into a field, we use component-wise addition, but a more clever choice of multiplication operation is:

$$(a, b) \cdot (c, d) := (ac - bd, ad + bc).$$

If we denote $(a, b) \in \mathbb{R}^2$ symbolically as $a + b\mathbf{i}$, then this multiplication operation becomes familiar complex multiplication:

$$(a + b\mathbf{i}) \cdot (c + d\mathbf{i}) = (ac - bd) + (ad + bc)\mathbf{i}.$$

It is straightforward to check that $\mathbb{R}^2$ is a field under these operations; it is usually denoted $\mathbb{C}$ and called the complex numbers.

3. The quaternions

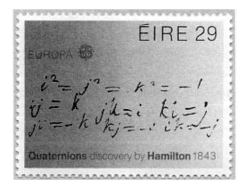

Is it possible to contrive a multiplication operation which, together with component-wise addition, makes $\mathbb{R}^n$ into a skew-field for $n > 2$? This is an important and difficult question. In 1843 Hamilton discovered that the answer is yes for $n = 4$.

To describe this multiplication rule, we will denote an element $(a, b, c, d) \in \mathbb{R}^4$ symbolically as $a + b\mathbf{i} + c\mathbf{j} + d\mathbf{k}$. We then define a multiplication rule for the symbols $\{1, \mathbf{i}, \mathbf{j}, \mathbf{k}\}$. The symbol "1" acts as expected:

$$\mathbf{i} \cdot 1 = 1 \cdot \mathbf{i} = \mathbf{i}, \qquad \mathbf{j} \cdot 1 = 1 \cdot \mathbf{j} = \mathbf{j} \qquad \mathbf{k} \cdot 1 = 1 \cdot \mathbf{k} = \mathbf{k}.$$

The other three symbols square to -1:

$$i^2 = j^2 = k^2 = -1.$$

Finally, the product of two of $\{i, j, k\}$ equals plus or minus the third:

$$i \cdot j = k, \qquad j \cdot k = i, \qquad k \cdot i = j,$$
$$j \cdot i = -k, \qquad k \cdot j = -i, \qquad i \cdot k = -j.$$

This sign convention can be remembered using Figure 2.

Figure 2. The quaternionic multiplication rule.

This multiplication rule for $\{1, i, j, k\}$ extends linearly to a multiplication on all of $\mathbb{R}^4$. For example,

$$\begin{aligned}
(2 + 3k) \cdot (i + 7j) &= 2i + 14j + 3ki + 21kj \\
&= 2i + 14j + 3j - 21i \\
&= -19i + 17j.
\end{aligned}$$

The product of two arbitrary elements has the following formula:

$$\begin{aligned}
(1.1) \quad (a + bi &+ cj + dk) \cdot (x + yi + zj + wk) \\
&= (ax - by - cz - dw) + (ay + bx + cw - dz)i \\
&\quad + (az + cx + dy - bw)j + (aw + dx + bz - cy)k.
\end{aligned}$$

The set $\mathbb{R}^4$, together with component-wise addition and the above-described multiplication operation, is denoted as $\mathbb{H}$ and called the quaternions. The quaternions have proven to be fundamental in several areas of math and physics. They are almost as important and as natural as the real and complex numbers.

To prove that $\mathbb{H}$ is a skew-field, the only difficult step is verifying that every non-zero element has a multiplicative inverse. For this, it

is useful to define the conjugate and the norm of an arbitrary element
$q = a + b\mathbf{i} + c\mathbf{j} + d\mathbf{k} \in \mathbb{H}$ as follows:

$$\bar{q} = a - b\mathbf{i} - c\mathbf{j} - d\mathbf{k}$$

$$|q| = \sqrt{a^2 + b^2 + c^2 + d^2}.$$

It is straightforward to check that $q \cdot \bar{q} = \bar{q} \cdot q = |q|^2$ and therefore
that $\frac{\bar{q}}{|q|^2}$ is a multiplicative inverse of q.

The rule for multiplying two quaternions with no $\mathbf{k}$ or $\mathbf{j}$ components agrees with our multiplication rule in $\mathbb{C}$. We therefore have
skew-field inclusions:

$$\mathbb{R} \subset \mathbb{C} \subset \mathbb{H}.$$

Any real number commutes with every element of $\mathbb{H}$. In Exercise 1.18,
you will show that only real numbers have this property. In particular,
every non-real complex numbers fails to commute with some elements
of $\mathbb{H}$.

Any complex number can be expressed as $z = a + b\mathbf{i}$ for some
$a, b \in \mathbb{R}$. Similarly, any quaternion can be expressed as $q = z + w\mathbf{j}$
for some $z, w \in \mathbb{C}$, since:

$$a + b\mathbf{i} + c\mathbf{j} + d\mathbf{k} = (a + b\mathbf{i}) + (c + d\mathbf{i})\mathbf{j}.$$

This analogy between $\mathbb{R} \subset \mathbb{C}$ and $\mathbb{C} \subset \mathbb{H}$ is often useful.

In this book, the elements of matrices are always either real, complex, or quaternionic numbers. Other fields, like $\mathbb{Q}$ or the finite fields,
are used in other branches of mathematics but for our purposes would
lead to a theory of matrices with insufficient geometric structure. We
want groups of matrices to have algebraic and geometric properties,
so we restrict to skew-fields that look like $\mathbb{R}^n$ for some n. This way,
groups of matrices are subsets of Euclidean spaces and therefore in-
herit geometric notions like distances and tangent vectors.

But is there a multiplication rule which makes $\mathbb{R}^n$ into a skew-
field for values of n other than $1, 2$ and 4? Do other (substantially
different) multiplication rules for $\mathbb{R}^1, \mathbb{R}^2$ and $\mathbb{R}^4$ exist? Can $\mathbb{R}^4$ be
made into a field rather than just a skew-field? The answer to all of
these questions is NO. More precisely, Frobenius proved in 1877 that
$\mathbb{R}, \mathbb{C}$ and $\mathbb{H}$ are the only associative real division algebras, up to the
natural notion of equivalence [4].

Definition 1.5. *An associative <u>real division algebra</u> is a real vector space, $\mathbb{K}$, with a multiplication rule, which is a skew-field under vector-addition and multiplication, such that for all $a \in \mathbb{R}$ and all $q_1, q_2 \in \mathbb{K}$:*

$$a(q_1 \cdot q_2) = (aq_1) \cdot q_2 = q_1 \cdot (aq_2).$$

The final hypothesis relates multiplication and scalar multiplication. It insures that $\mathbb{K}$ has a sub-field isomorphic to $\mathbb{R}$, namely, all scalar multiples of the multiplicative identity 1.

We will not prove Frobenius' theorem; we require it only for reassurance that we are not omitting any important number systems from our discussion. There is an important multiplication rule for $\mathbb{R}^8$, called <u>octonian</u> multiplication, but it is not associative, so it makes $\mathbb{R}^8$ into something weaker than a skew-field. We will not consider the octonians.

In this book, $\mathbb{K}$ always denotes one of $\{\mathbb{R}, \mathbb{C}, \mathbb{H}\}$, except where stated otherwise.

4. Matrix operations

In this section, we briefly review basic notation and properties of matrices. Let $M_{m,n}(\mathbb{K})$ denote the set of all m by n matrices with entries in $\mathbb{K}$. For example,

$$M_{2,3}(\mathbb{C}) = \left\{ \begin{pmatrix} z_{11} & z_{12} & z_{13} \\ z_{21} & z_{22} & z_{23} \end{pmatrix} \Big| z_{ij} \in \mathbb{C} \right\}.$$

Denote the space $M_{n,n}(\mathbb{K})$ of <u>square matrices</u> as simply $M_n(\mathbb{K})$. If $A \in M_{m,n}(\mathbb{K})$, then A_{ij} denotes the element in row i and column j of A.

Addition of same-dimension matrices is defined component-wise, so that

$$(A + B)_{ij} = A_{ij} + B_{ij}.$$

The product of $A \in M_{m,n}(\mathbb{K})$ and $B \in M_{n,l}(\mathbb{K})$ is the element $AB \in M_{m,l}(\mathbb{K})$ defined by the familiar formula:

$$(1.2) \qquad (AB)_{ij} = (\text{row } i \text{ of } A) \cdot (\text{column } j \text{ of } B) = \sum_{s=1}^{n} A_{is} \cdot B_{sj}.$$

Matrix multiplication is not generally commutative.

Denote a diagonal matrix as in this example:

$$\mathrm{diag}(1,2,3) = \begin{pmatrix} 1 & 0 & 0 \\ 0 & 2 & 0 \\ 0 & 0 & 3 \end{pmatrix}.$$

The identity matrix is:

$$I = \mathrm{diag}(1,...,1).$$

The transpose of $A \in M_{m,n}(\mathbb{K})$ is the matrix $A^T \in M_{n,m}$ obtained by interchanging the rows and columns of A, so that:

$$(A^T)_{ij} = A_{ji}.$$

For example,

$$\begin{pmatrix} 1 & 2 \\ 3 & 4 \\ 5 & 6 \end{pmatrix}^T = \begin{pmatrix} 1 & 3 & 5 \\ 2 & 4 & 6 \end{pmatrix}.$$

It is straightforward to check that

$$(1.3) \qquad\qquad (A \cdot B)^T = B^T \cdot A^T$$

for any matrices A and B of compatible dimensions to be multiplied.

Matrix multiplication and addition interact as follows:

Proposition 1.6. *For all* $A, B, C \in M_n(\mathbb{K})$,

    (1) $A \cdot (B \cdot C) = (A \cdot B) \cdot C$.

    (2) $(A + B) \cdot C = A \cdot C + B \cdot C$ *and* $C \cdot (A + B) = C \cdot A + C \cdot B$.

    (3) $A \cdot I = I \cdot A = A$.

The trace of a square matrix $A \in M_n(\mathbb{K})$ is defined as the sum of its diagonal entries:

$$\mathrm{trace}(A) = A_{11} + \cdots + A_{nn}.$$

When $\mathbb{K} \in \{\mathbb{R}, \mathbb{C}\}$, we have the familiar property for $A, B \in M_n(\mathbb{K})$:

$$(1.4) \qquad\qquad \mathrm{trace}(AB) = \mathrm{trace}(BA).$$

Since multiplication in $\mathbb{H}$ is not commutative, this property is false even in $M_1(\mathbb{H})$.

When $\mathbb{K} \in \{\mathbb{R}, \mathbb{C}\}$, the <u>determinant</u> function,

$$\det : M_n(\mathbb{K}) \to \mathbb{K},$$

is familiar. It can be defined recursively by declaring that the determinant of $A \in M_1(\mathbb{K})$ equals its single element, and the determinant of $A \in M_{n+1}(\mathbb{K})$ is defined in terms of determinants of elements of $M_n(\mathbb{K})$ by the expansion of minors formula:

$$(1.5) \qquad \det(A) := \sum_{j=1}^{n+1} (-1)^{j+1} \cdot A_{1j} \cdot \det(A[1,j]),$$

where $A[i,j] \in M_n(\mathbb{K})$ is the matrix obtained by crossing out row i and column j from A. For example,

$$\begin{pmatrix} a & b & c \\ d & e & f \\ g & h & i \end{pmatrix} [2,1] = \begin{pmatrix} b & c \\ h & i \end{pmatrix}.$$

Thus, the determinant of a 3×3 matrix is:

$$\det \begin{pmatrix} a & b & c \\ d & e & f \\ g & h & i \end{pmatrix} = a \cdot \det \begin{pmatrix} e & f \\ h & i \end{pmatrix} - b \cdot \det \begin{pmatrix} d & f \\ g & i \end{pmatrix}$$

$$+ c \cdot \det \begin{pmatrix} d & e \\ g & h \end{pmatrix}$$

$$= a(ei - fh) - b(di - fg) + c(dh - eg)$$

$$= aei + bfg + cdh - (afh + bdi + ceg).$$

It is clear that $\det(I) = 1$. In a linear algebra course, one proves that for all $A, B \in M_n(\mathbb{K})$,

$$(1.6) \qquad \det(A \cdot B) = \det(A) \cdot \det(B).$$

We postpone defining the determinant of a quaternionic matrix until the next chapter. Exercise 1.5 at the end of this chapter demonstrates why Equation 1.5 is insufficient when $\mathbb{K} = \mathbb{H}$.

Let $\mathbb{K} \in \{\mathbb{R}, \mathbb{C}, \mathbb{H}\}$. When $a \in \mathbb{K}$ and $A \in M_{n,m}(\mathbb{K})$, we define $a \cdot A \in M_{n,m}(\mathbb{K})$ to be the result of left-multiplying the elements of A by a:

$$(a \cdot A)_{ij} := a \cdot A_{ij}.$$

This operation is called left scalar multiplication. The operations of matrix addition and left scalar multiplication make $M_{n,m}(\mathbb{K})$ into a *left vector space* over $\mathbb{K}$.

Definition 1.7. *A left vector space over a skew-field $\mathbb{K}$ is a set M with an addition operation from $M \times M$ to M (denoted $A, B \mapsto A+B$) and scalar multiplication operation from $\mathbb{K} \times M$ to M (denoted $a, A \mapsto a \cdot A$) such that M is an abelian group under addition, and for all $a, b \in \mathbb{K}$ and all $A, B \in M$,*

(1) $a \cdot (b \cdot A) = (a \cdot b) \cdot A$.

(2) $1 \cdot A = A$.

(3) $(a + b) \cdot A = a \cdot A + b \cdot A$.

(4) $a \cdot (A + B) = a \cdot A + a \cdot B$.

This exactly matches the familiar definition of a vector space. Familiar terminology for vector spaces over fields, like subspaces, bases, linear independence, and dimension, make sense for left vector spaces over skew-fields. For example:

Definition 1.8. *A subset W of a left vector space V over a skew-field $\mathbb{K}$ is called a $\mathbb{K}$-subspace (or just a subspace) if for all $a, b \in \mathbb{K}$ and all $A, B \in W$, $a \cdot A + b \cdot B \in W$.*

If we had instead chosen *right* scalar multiplication in $M_{n,m}(\mathbb{K})$, defined as $(A \cdot a)_{ij} := A_{ij} \cdot a$, then $M_{n,m}(\mathbb{K})$ would have become a *right vector space* over $\mathbb{K}$. In a right vector space, scalar multiplication is denoted $a, A \mapsto A \cdot a$. Properties (2) through (4) of Definition 1.7 must be re-written to reflect this notational change. Property (1) is special because the change is more than just notational:

(1') $(A \cdot a) \cdot b = A \cdot (a \cdot b)$.

Do you see the difference? The net effect of multiplying A by a and then by b is to multiply A by ba in a left vector space, or by ab in a right vector space.

When $\mathbb{K}$ is a field, the difference between a left and a right vector space over $\mathbb{K}$ is an irrelevant notational distinction, so one speaks simply of "vector spaces". But when $\mathbb{K} = \mathbb{H}$, it makes an essential difference that we are henceforth adopting the convention of left scalar multiplication, and thereby choosing to regard $M_{n,m}(\mathbb{H})$ as a left vector space over $\mathbb{H}$.

5. Matrices as linear transformations

One cornerstone of a linear algebra course is the discovery that matrices correspond to linear transformations, and vice versa. We now review that discovery. Extra care is needed when $\mathbb{K} = \mathbb{H}$.

Definition 1.9. *Suppose that V_1 and V_2 are left vector spaces over $\mathbb{K}$. A function $f : V_1 \to V_2$ is called $\underline{\mathbb{K}\text{-linear}}$ (or simply $\underline{linear}$) if for all $a, b \in \mathbb{K}$ and all $X, Y \in V_1$,*

$$f(a \cdot X + b \cdot Y) = a \cdot f(X) + b \cdot f(Y).$$

It is natural to identify $\mathbb{K}^n = \{(q_1, ..., q_n) \mid q_i \in \mathbb{K}\}$ with $M_{1,n}(\mathbb{K})$ (horizontal single-row matrices) and thereby regard $\mathbb{K}^n$ as a left vector space over $\mathbb{K}$. Using this identification, there are two potential ways in which matrices might correspond to linear transformations from $\mathbb{K}^n$ to $\mathbb{K}^n$:

Definition 1.10. *If $A \in M_n(\mathbb{K})$, define $R_A : \mathbb{K}^n \to \mathbb{K}^n$ and define $L_A : \mathbb{K}^n \to \mathbb{K}^n$ such that for $X \in \mathbb{K}^n$,*

$$R_A(X) := X \cdot A \quad and \quad L_A(X) := (A \cdot X^T)^T.$$

For example, if $A = \begin{pmatrix} 1 & 2 \\ 3 & 4 \end{pmatrix} \in M_2(\mathbb{R})$, then for $(x, y) \in \mathbb{R}^2$,

$$R_A(x, y) = \begin{pmatrix} x & y \end{pmatrix} \cdot \begin{pmatrix} 1 & 2 \\ 3 & 4 \end{pmatrix} = (x + 3y, 2x + 4y), \text{ and}$$

$$L_A(x, y) = \left(\begin{pmatrix} 1 & 2 \\ 3 & 4 \end{pmatrix} \cdot \begin{pmatrix} x \\ y \end{pmatrix} \right)^T = \begin{pmatrix} x + 2y \\ 3x + 4y \end{pmatrix}^T = (x + 2y, 3x + 4y).$$

We first prove that *right* multiplication determines a one-to-one correspondence between linear functions from $\mathbb{K}^n$ to $\mathbb{K}^n$ and matrices.

Proposition 1.11.

(1) *For any $A \in M_n(\mathbb{K})$, $R_A : \mathbb{K}^n \to \mathbb{K}^n$ is $\mathbb{K}$-linear.*

(2) *Each $\mathbb{K}$-linear function from $\mathbb{K}^n$ to $\mathbb{K}^n$ equals R_A for some $A \in M_n(\mathbb{K})$.*

Proof. To prove (1), notice that for all $a, b \in \mathbb{K}$ and $X, Y \in \mathbb{K}^n$,

$$R_A(aX + bY) = (aX + bY) \cdot A = a(X \cdot A) + b(Y \cdot A)$$
$$= a \cdot R_A(X) + b \cdot R_A(Y).$$

To prove (2), assume that $f : \mathbb{K}^n \to \mathbb{K}^n$ is $\mathbb{K}$-linear. Let $A \in M_n(\mathbb{K})$ denote the matrix whose ith row is $f(e_i)$, where

$$e_1 = (1, 0, ..., 0), e_2 = (0, 1, 0, ..., 0), ..., e_n = (0, ..., 0, 1)$$

denotes the standard basis for $\mathbb{K}^n$. It's easy to see that $f(e_i) = R_A(e_i)$ for all $i = 1, .., n$. Since f and R_A are both linear maps and they agree on a basis, we conclude that $f = R_A$. □

We see from the proof that the rows of $A \in M_n(\mathbb{K})$ are the images under R_A of $\{e_1, ..., e_n\}$. Similarly, the columns are the images under L_A.

Most linear algebra textbooks use the convention of identifying a matrix $A \in M_n(\mathbb{K})$ with the function $L_A : \mathbb{K}^n \to \mathbb{K}^n$. Unfortunately, this function is necessarily $\mathbb{K}$-linear only when $\mathbb{K} \in \{\mathbb{R}, \mathbb{C}\}$.

Proposition 1.12. *Let* $\mathbb{K} \in \{\mathbb{R}, \mathbb{C}\}$.

(1) *For any* $A \in M_n(\mathbb{K})$, $L_A : \mathbb{K}^n \to \mathbb{K}^n$ *is* $\mathbb{K}$-*linear.*

(2) *Each* $\mathbb{K}$-*linear function from* $\mathbb{K}^n$ *to* $\mathbb{K}^n$ *equals* L_A *for some* $A \in M_n(\mathbb{K})$.

Proposition 1.12 is an immediate corollary of Proposition 1.11 plus the following easily verified fact:

$$L_A = R_{A^T} \text{ for all } A \in M_n(\mathbb{R}) \text{ or } A \in M_n(\mathbb{C}).$$

Our previous decision to consider $\mathbb{H}^n$ as a *left* vector space over $\mathbb{H}$ forces us now to use the correspondence $A \leftrightarrow R_A$ between matrices and linear transformations (rather than $A \leftrightarrow L_A$), at least when we wish to include $\mathbb{K} = \mathbb{H}$ in our discussion.

Under either correspondence between matrices and transformations, matrix multiplication corresponds to composition of transformations, since:

$$L_A(L_B(X)) = L_{A \cdot B}(X) \text{ and } R_A(R_B(X)) = R_{B \cdot A}(X).$$

In a linear algebra course, this is one's first indication that the initially unmotivated definition of matrix multiplication is in fact quite natural.

6. The general linear groups

The set $M_n(\mathbb{K})$ is not a group under matrix multiplication because some matrices do not have multiplicative inverses. For example, if $A \in M_n(\mathbb{K})$ has all entries zero, then A has no multiplicative inverse; that is, there is no matrix B for which $AB = BA = I$. However, the elements of $M_n(\mathbb{K})$ which do have inverses form a very important group whose subgroups are the main topic of this text.

Definition 1.13. *The general linear group over* $\mathbb{K}$ *is:*

$$GL_n(\mathbb{K}) := \{A \in M_n(\mathbb{K}) \mid \exists B \in M_n(\mathbb{K}) \text{ with } AB = BA = I\}.$$

Such a matrix B is the multiplicative inverse of A and is therefore denoted A^{-1}. As its name suggests, $GL_n(\mathbb{K})$ is a group under the operation of matrix multiplication (why?). The following more visual characterization of the general linear group is often useful:

Proposition 1.14.

$$GL_n(\mathbb{K}) = \{A \in M_n(\mathbb{K}) \mid R_A : \mathbb{K}^n \to \mathbb{K}^n \text{ is a linear isomorphism}\}.$$

For $A \in M_n(\mathbb{K})$, R_A is always linear; it is called an isomorphism if it is invertible (or equivalently, surjective, or equivalently, injective). Thus, general linear matrices correspond to motions of $\mathbb{K}^n$ with no collapsing.

Proof. If $A \in GL_n(\mathbb{K})$ and B is such that $BA = I$, then

$$R_A \circ R_B = R_{BA} = R_I = \text{id (the identity)},$$

so R_A has inverse R_B.

Conversely, let $A \in M_n(\mathbb{K})$ be such that R_A is invertible. The map $(R_A)^{-1}$ is linear, which can be seen by applying R_A to both sides of the following equation:

$$(R_A)^{-1}(aX + bY) \stackrel{?}{=} a(R_A)^{-1}(X) + b(R_A)^{-1}(Y).$$

Since every linear map is represented by a matrix, $(R_A)^{-1} = R_B$ for some $B \in M_n(\mathbb{K})$. Therefore, $R_{BA} = R_A \circ R_B = \text{id}$, which implies $BA = I$. Similarly, $R_{AB} = R_B \circ R_A = \text{id}$, which implies $AB = I$. $\quad\square$

The following well-known fact from linear algebra provides yet another useful description of the general linear group, at least when $\mathbb{K} \neq \mathbb{H}$:

Proposition 1.15. *If* $\mathbb{K} \in \{\mathbb{R}, \mathbb{C}\}$, *then*

$$GL_n(\mathbb{K}) = \{A \in M_n(\mathbb{K}) \mid \det(A) \neq 0\}.$$

In fact, the elements of the inverse of a matrix can be described explicitly in terms of the determinant of the matrix and its minors:

Proposition 1.16 (Cramer's rule). *Let* $\mathbb{K} \in \{\mathbb{R}, \mathbb{C}\}$. *Using the notation of Equation 1.5,*

$$(A^{-1})_{ij} = (-1)^{i+j} \frac{\det(A[j, i])}{\det(A)}.$$

7. Change of basis via conjugation

In this section, we review a basic fact from linear algebra: a conjugate of a matrix represents the same linear transformation as the matrix, but in a different basis.

Let $\mathfrak{g}$ denote an n-dimensional (left) vector space over $\mathbb{K}$. Then $\mathfrak{g}$ is isomorphic to $\mathbb{K}^n$. In fact, there are many isomorphisms from $\mathfrak{g}$ to $\mathbb{K}^n$. For any ordered basis $V = \{v_1, ..., v_n\}$ of $\mathfrak{g}$, the following is an isomorphism:

$$(1.7) \qquad\qquad (c_1 v_1 + \cdots + c_n v_n) \mapsto (c_1, ..., c_n).$$

Every isomorphism from $\mathfrak{g}$ to $\mathbb{K}^n$ has this form for some ordered basis of $\mathfrak{g}$, so choosing an isomorphism amounts to choosing an ordered basis. In practice, there is typically no choice of basis which seems more natural than the other choices. To convince yourself of this, consider the case where $\mathfrak{g}$ is an arbitrary subspace of $\mathbb{K}^m$ for some $m > n$.

Now suppose that $f : \mathfrak{g} \to \mathfrak{g}$ is a linear transformation. In order to identify f with a matrix, we must first choose an ordered basis V

of $\mathfrak{g}$. We use this basis to identify $\mathfrak{g} \cong \mathbb{K}^n$ and thereby to regard f as a linear transformation from $\mathbb{K}^n$ to $\mathbb{K}^n$, which can be represented as R_A for some $A \in M_n(\mathbb{K})$. A crucial point is that A depends on the choice of ordered basis. To emphasize this dependence, we say that "A represents f in the basis V (via right-multiplication)." We would like to determine which matrix represents f in a different basis.

To avoid cumbersome notation, we will simplify this problem without really losing generality. Suppose that $f : \mathbb{K}^n \to \mathbb{K}^n$ is a linear transformation. We know that $f = R_A$ for some $A \in M_n(\mathbb{K})$. Translating this sentence into our new terminology, we say that "A represents f in the standard basis of $\mathbb{K}^n$," which is:

$$\{e_1 = (1, 0, ..., 0), e_2 = (0, 1, 0, ..., 0), ..., e_n = (0, ..., 0, 1)\}.$$

Now let $V = \{v_1, ..., v_n\}$ denote an arbitrary basis of $\mathbb{K}^n$. We seek the matrix which represents f in the basis V. First, we let $g \in GL_n(\mathbb{K})$ denote the matrix whose rows are $v_1, v_2, ..., v_n$. We call g the change of basis matrix. To understand why, notice that $e_i g = v_i$ for each $i = 1, ..., n$. So,

$$(c_1, ..., c_n) \cdot g = (c_1 e_1 + \cdots + c_n e_n) \cdot g = c_1 v_1 + \cdots + c_n v_n.$$

By Equation 1.7, the vector $c_1 v_1 + \cdots + c_n v_n \in \mathbb{K}^n$ is represented in the basis V as the vector $(c_1, ..., c_n)$. Thus, $R_g : \mathbb{K}^n \to \mathbb{K}^n$ translates between V and the standard basis. For $X \in \mathbb{K}^n$, $R_g(X)$ represents in the standard basis the same vector that X represents in V. Further, $R_{g^{-1}}(X)$ represents in V the same vector that X represents in the standard basis.

Proposition 1.17. gAg^{-1} *represents* f *in the basis* V.

Proof. Let $X = (c_1, ..., c_n)$, which represents $c_1 v_1 + \cdots + c_n v_n$ in V. We must show that $R_{gAg^{-1}}(X)$ represents $(c_1 v_1 + \cdots + c_n v_n) \cdot A$ in V. This follows from:

$$R_{gAg^{-1}}(X) = (c_1, ..., c_n) g A g^{-1} = (c_1 v_1 + \cdots + c_n v_n) A g^{-1}$$
$$= R_{g^{-1}}((c_1 v_1 + \cdots + c_n v_n) \cdot A).$$

$\square$

Proposition 1.17 can be summarized in the following way: for any $A \in M_n(\mathbb{K})$ and any $g \in GL_n(\mathbb{K})$, the matrix gAg^{-1} represents R_A in the basis $\{e_1 g, ..., e_n g\}$.

The basic idea of the proof was simple enough: the transformation $R_{gAg^{-1}} = R_{g^{-1}} \circ R_A \circ R_g$ first translates into the standard basis, then performs the transformation associated to A, then translates back.

This key result requires only slight modification when representing linear transformations using *left* matrix multiplication when $\mathbb{K}$ is $\mathbb{R}$ or $\mathbb{C}$: for any $A \in M_n(\mathbb{K})$ and any $g \in GL_n(\mathbb{K})$, the matrix $g^{-1}Ag$ represents L_A in the basis $\{g e_1, ..., g e_n\}$ (via left multiplication). The proof idea is the same: $L_{g^{-1}Ag} = L_{g^{-1}} \circ L_A \circ L_g$ first translates into the standard basis, then performs the transformation associated to A, then translates back.

8. Exercises

Ex. 1.1. Describe a natural 1-to-1 correspondence between elements of $SO(3)$ and elements of

$$T^1 S^2 = \{(p, v) \in \mathbb{R}^3 \times \mathbb{R}^3 \mid |p| = |v| = 1 \text{ and } p \perp v\},$$

which can be thought of as the collection of all unit-length vectors v tangent to all points p of S^2. Compare to Question 1.2.

Ex. 1.2. Prove Equation 1.3.

Ex. 1.3. Prove Equation 1.4.

Ex. 1.4. Let $A, B \in M_n(\mathbb{K})$. Prove that if $AB = I$, then $BA = I$.

Ex. 1.5. Suppose that the determinant of $A \in M_n(\mathbb{H})$ were defined as in Equation 1.5. Show for $A = \begin{pmatrix} i & j \\ i & j \end{pmatrix} \in M_2(\mathbb{H})$ that $\det(A) \neq 0$ but $R_A : \mathbb{H}^2 \to \mathbb{H}^2$ is not invertible.

Ex. 1.6. Find $B \in M_2(\mathbb{R})$ such that $R_B : \mathbb{R}^2 \to \mathbb{R}^2$ is a counterclockwise rotation through an angle θ.

Ex. 1.7. Describe all elements $A \in GL_n(\mathbb{R})$ with the property that $AB = BA$ for all $B \in GL_n(\mathbb{R})$.

Ex. 1.8. Let $SL_2(\mathbb{Z})$ denote the set of all 2 by 2 matrices with integer entries and with determinant 1. Prove that $SL_2(\mathbb{Z})$ is a subgroup of $GL_2(\mathbb{R})$. Is $SL_n(\mathbb{Z})$ (defined analogously) a subgroup of $GL_n(\mathbb{R})$?

Ex. 1.9. Describe the product of two matrices in $M_6(\mathbb{K})$ which both have the form:

$$\begin{pmatrix} a & b & 0 & 0 & 0 & 0 \\ c & d & 0 & 0 & 0 & 0 \\ 0 & 0 & e & f & g & 0 \\ 0 & 0 & h & i & j & 0 \\ 0 & 0 & k & l & m & 0 \\ 0 & 0 & 0 & 0 & 0 & n \end{pmatrix}$$

Describe a general rule for the product of two matrices with the same *block form*.

Ex. 1.10. If $G_1 \subset GL_{n_1}(\mathbb{K})$ and $G_2 \subset GL_{n_2}(\mathbb{K})$ are subgroups, describe a subgroup of $GL_{n_1+n_2}(\mathbb{K})$ which is isomorphic to $G_1 \times G_2$.

Ex. 1.11. Show by example that for $A \in M_n(\mathbb{H})$, $L_A : \mathbb{H}^n \to \mathbb{H}^n$ is not necessarily $\mathbb{H}$-linear.

Ex. 1.12. Define the *real* and *imaginary* parts of a quaternion as follows:

$$\mathrm{Re}(a + b\mathbf{i} + c\mathbf{j} + d\mathbf{k}) = a$$

$$\mathrm{Im}(a + b\mathbf{i} + c\mathbf{j} + d\mathbf{k}) = b\mathbf{i} + c\mathbf{j} + d\mathbf{k}.$$

Let $q_1 = x_1\mathbf{i} + y_1\mathbf{j} + z_1\mathbf{k}$ and $q_2 = x_2\mathbf{i} + y_2\mathbf{j} + z_2\mathbf{k}$ be *purely imaginary* quaternions in $\mathbb{H}$. Prove that $-\mathrm{Re}(q_1 \cdot q_2)$ is their vector dot product in $\mathbb{R}^3 = \mathrm{span}\{\mathbf{i}, \mathbf{j}, \mathbf{k}\}$ and $\mathrm{Im}(q_1 \cdot q_2)$ is their vector cross product.

Ex. 1.13. Prove that non-real elements $q_1, q_2 \in \mathbb{H}$ commute if and only if their imaginary parts are parallel; that is, $\mathrm{Im}(q_1) = \lambda \cdot \mathrm{Im}(q_2)$ for some $\lambda \in \mathbb{R}$.

Ex. 1.14. Characterize the pairs $q_1, q_2 \in \mathbb{H}$ which anti-commute, meaning that $q_1 q_2 = -q_2 q_1$.

Ex. 1.15. If $q \in \mathbb{H}$ satisfies $q\mathbf{i} = \mathbf{i}q$, prove that $q \in \mathbb{C}$.

Ex. 1.16. Prove that complex multiplication in $\mathbb{C} \cong \mathbb{R}^2$ does not extend to a multiplication operation on $\mathbb{R}^3$ which makes $\mathbb{R}^3$ into a real division algebra.

Ex. 1.17. Describe a subgroup of $GL_{n+1}(\mathbb{R})$ which is isomorphic to the group $\mathbb{R}^n$ under the operation of vector-addition.

Ex. 1.18. If $\lambda \in \mathbb{H}$ commutes with every element of $\mathbb{H}$, prove that $\lambda \in \mathbb{R}$.

Chapter 2

All matrix groups are real matrix groups

This book is about subgroups of the general linear groups. In this chapter, we prove that every subgroup of $GL_n(\mathbb{C})$ or $GL_n(\mathbb{H})$ is isomorphic to a subgroup of $GL_m(\mathbb{R})$ for some m. Thus, this book is about subgroups of the *real* general linear group. The result is an immediate consequence of:

Theorem 2.1.

    (1) $GL_n(\mathbb{C})$ *is isomorphic to a subgroup of* $GL_{2n}(\mathbb{R})$.

    (2) $GL_n(\mathbb{H})$ *is isomorphic to a subgroup of* $GL_{2n}(\mathbb{C})$.

It follows that $GL_n(\mathbb{H})$ is isomorphic to a subgroup of $GL_{4n}(\mathbb{R})$. We will prove Theorem 2.1 by constructing injective homomorphisms:

$$\rho_n : GL_n(\mathbb{C}) \to GL_{2n}(\mathbb{R}) \ \text{ and } \ \Psi_n : GL_n(\mathbb{H}) \to GL_{2n}(\mathbb{C}).$$

These homomorphisms play an important role in the remainder of the text.

Many important groups are much more naturally regarded as subgroups of $GL_n(\mathbb{H})$ or $GL_n(\mathbb{C})$ rather than of $GL_m(\mathbb{R})$, so the theorem does not obviate our future need to consider the cases $\mathbb{K} = \mathbb{C}$ and $\mathbb{K} = \mathbb{H}$.

1. Complex matrices as real matrices

In Exercise 1.6, you showed for the matrix

$$B = \begin{pmatrix} \cos\theta & \sin\theta \\ -\sin\theta & \cos\theta \end{pmatrix} \in M_2(\mathbb{R})$$

that $R_B : \mathbb{R}^2 \to \mathbb{R}^2$ is a counterclockwise rotation through angle θ. In fact, standard trigonometric identities give that for all $r, \phi \in \mathbb{R}$:

$$R_B(r\cos\phi, r\sin\phi) = (r\cos(\theta + \phi), r\sin(\theta + \phi)).$$

Compare this to the matrix $A = (e^{i\theta}) \in M_1(\mathbb{C})$. For this matrix, $R_A : \mathbb{C}^1 \to \mathbb{C}^1$ is also a counterclockwise rotation through angle θ, since

$$R_A(re^{i\phi}) = re^{i(\theta + \phi)}.$$

Thus, $A \in M_1(\mathbb{C})$ and $B \in M_2(\mathbb{R})$ "represent the same motion".

More generally, we wish to construct a function

$$\rho_n : M_n(\mathbb{C}) \to M_{2n}(\mathbb{R})$$

which sends $A \in M_n(\mathbb{C})$ to the matrix $B \in M_{2n}(\mathbb{R})$ that "represents the same motion". More precisely, every $A \in M_n(\mathbb{C})$ corresponds to a linear transformation $R_A : \mathbb{C}^n \to \mathbb{C}^n$. This transformation can instead be thought of as a transformation from $\mathbb{R}^{2n}$ to $\mathbb{R}^{2n}$, since $\mathbb{R}^{2n}$ is naturally identified with $\mathbb{C}^n$ via the bijection $f_n : \mathbb{C}^n \to \mathbb{R}^{2n}$ defined as:

$$f_n(a_1 + b_1\mathbf{i}, a_2 + b_2\mathbf{i}, ..., a_n + b_n\mathbf{i}) := (a_1, b_1, a_2, b_2, ..., a_n, b_n).$$

This transformation from $\mathbb{R}^{2n}$ to $\mathbb{R}^{2n}$ is represented as R_B for some $B \in M_{2n}(\mathbb{R})$.

How do we determine B from A? Asked differently, how do we define a function

$$\rho_n : M_n(\mathbb{C}) \to M_{2n}(\mathbb{R})$$

such that the following diagram commutes for all $A \in M_n(\mathbb{C})$:

(2.1)

$$\begin{array}{ccc} \mathbb{C}^n & \xrightarrow{f_n} & \mathbb{R}^{2n} \\ {\scriptstyle R_A}\downarrow & & \downarrow{\scriptstyle R_{\rho_n(A)}} \\ \mathbb{C}^n & \xrightarrow{f_n} & \mathbb{R}^{2n} \end{array}$$

(the diagram is said to <u>commute</u> if $R_{\rho_n(A)} \circ f_n = f_n \circ R_A$; that is, if right-then-down equals down-then-right). When $n = 1$, it is straightforward to check that the function $\rho_1 : M_1(\mathbb{C}) \to M_2(\mathbb{R})$ defined as follows makes diagram 2.1 commute:

$$\rho_1(a + b\mathbf{i}) := \begin{pmatrix} a & b \\ -b & a \end{pmatrix}.$$

Notice that ρ_1 relates the matrices A and B of the previous discussion, since

$$\rho_1(e^{i\theta}) = \rho_1(\cos\theta + \mathbf{i}\sin\theta) = \begin{pmatrix} \cos\theta & \sin\theta \\ -\sin\theta & \cos\theta \end{pmatrix} \in M_2(\mathbb{R}).$$

For $A \in M_n(\mathbb{C})$ with $n > 1$, we build $\rho_n(A)$ out of 2-by-2 blocks equal to ρ_1 applied to the entries of A. For example,

$$\rho_2 \begin{pmatrix} a + b\mathbf{i} & c + d\mathbf{i} \\ e + f\mathbf{i} & h + j\mathbf{i} \end{pmatrix} = \begin{pmatrix} a & b & c & d \\ -b & a & -d & c \\ e & f & h & j \\ -f & e & -j & h \end{pmatrix},$$

and so on. In Exercise 2.1, you will prove that this definition of ρ_n makes diagram 2.1 commute.

Proposition 2.2. *For all $\lambda \in \mathbb{R}$ and $A, B \in M_n(\mathbb{C})$,*

   (1) $\rho_n(\lambda \cdot A) = \lambda \cdot \rho_n(A)$.

   (2) $\rho_n(A + B) = \rho_n(A) + \rho_n(B)$.

   (3) $\rho_n(A \cdot B) = \rho_n(A) \cdot \rho_n(B)$.

Proof. Parts (1) and (2) are immediate from definition. For part (3), consider the commutative diagram:

$$
\begin{array}{ccc}
\mathbb{C}^n & \xrightarrow{\ f_n\ } & \mathbb{R}^{2n} \\
{\scriptstyle R_A}\Big\downarrow & & \Big\downarrow{\scriptstyle R_{\rho_n(A)}} \\
\mathbb{C}^n & \xrightarrow{\ f_n\ } & \mathbb{R}^{2n} \\
{\scriptstyle R_B}\Big\downarrow & & \Big\downarrow{\scriptstyle R_{\rho_n(B)}} \\
\mathbb{C}^n & \xrightarrow{\ f_n\ } & \mathbb{R}^{2n}
\end{array}
$$

The composition of the two down-arrows on the right is

$$R_{\rho_n(B)} \circ R_{\rho_n(A)} = R_{\rho_n(A) \cdot \rho_n(B)}.$$

On the other hand, since on the left $R_B \circ R_A = R_{AB}$, this composition on the right also equals $R_{\rho_n(AB)}$. In summary,

$$R_{\rho_n(A) \cdot \rho_n(B)} = R_{\rho_n(AB)},$$

which implies that $\rho_n(A) \cdot \rho_n(B) = \rho_n(AB)$. $\square$

It is easy to see that $\rho_n : M_n(\mathbb{C}) \to M_{2n}(\mathbb{R})$ is injective but not surjective.

Definition 2.3. *Matrices of $M_{2n}(\mathbb{R})$ in the image of ρ_n are called* <u>complex-linear</u> *real matrices.*

The terminology is justified by the following proposition, whose proof is immediate.

Proposition 2.4. $B \in M_{2n}(\mathbb{R})$ *is complex-linear if and only if the function* $f_n^{-1} \circ R_B \circ f_n : \mathbb{C}^n \to \mathbb{C}^n$ *is a $\mathbb{C}$-linear transformation:*

$$
\begin{array}{ccc}
\mathbb{C}^n & \xrightarrow{\ f_n\ } & \mathbb{R}^{2n} \\
 & & \Big\downarrow{R_B} \\
\mathbb{C}^n & \xleftarrow{\ f_n^{-1}\ } & \mathbb{R}^{2n}
\end{array}
$$

The function $F = f_n^{-1} \circ R_B \circ f_n$ is always $\mathbb{R}$-linear (which makes sense because $\mathbb{C}^n$ can be regarded as a vector space over $\mathbb{R}$). It is $\mathbb{C}$-linear if and only if $F(\mathbf{i} \cdot X) = \mathbf{i} \cdot F(X)$ for all $X \in \mathbb{C}^n$. So the complex linear real matrices are the ones that "commute with $\mathbf{i}$" in this sense. There is an important way to re-describe this idea of a real matrix commuting with $\mathbf{i}$. Define $J_{2n} = \rho_n(\mathbf{i} \cdot I)$, so for example,

$$
J_4 = \begin{pmatrix} 0 & 1 & 0 & 0 \\ -1 & 0 & 0 & 0 \\ 0 & 0 & 0 & 1 \\ 0 & 0 & -1 & 0 \end{pmatrix}.
$$

Notice that $J_{2n}^2 = -1 \cdot I$ and that the following diagram commutes:

$$\mathbb{C}^n \xrightarrow{\;f_n\;} \mathbb{R}^{2n}$$

$$R_{\mathbf{i}\cdot I} = \text{(scalar mult. by i)} \Big\downarrow \qquad\qquad \Big\downarrow R_{J_{2n}}$$

$$\mathbb{C}^n \xrightarrow{\;f_n\;} \mathbb{R}^{2n}$$

The matrix J_{2n} is called the standard complex structure on R^{2n}. Why? Because, compared to $\mathbb{R}^{2n}$, the space $\mathbb{C}^n$ has the additional structure of scalar-multiplication by $\mathbf{i}$. This extra structure is mimicked in $\mathbb{R}^{2n}$ by $R_{J_{2n}}$. This allows an improved verbalization of the above-indicated idea that complex-linear real matrices "commute with $\mathbf{i}$":

Proposition 2.5. $B \in M_{2n}(\mathbb{R})$ is complex-linear if and only if

$$B \cdot J_{2n} = J_{2n} \cdot B.$$

Proof. Suppose that $B \in M_{2n}(\mathbb{R})$ is complex-linear, so there is a matrix $A \in M_n(\mathbb{C})$ for which the following diagram commutes:

$$\mathbb{C}^n \xrightarrow{\;f_n\;} \mathbb{R}^{2n}$$

$$\text{(scalar mult. by i)} \Big\downarrow \qquad\qquad \Big\downarrow R_{J_{2n}}$$

$$\mathbb{C}^n \xrightarrow{\;f_n\;} \mathbb{R}^{2n}$$

$$R_A \Big\downarrow \qquad\qquad \Big\downarrow R_B$$

$$\mathbb{C}^n \xrightarrow{\;f_n\;} \mathbb{R}^{2n}$$

$$\text{(scalar mult. by i)} \Big\downarrow \qquad\qquad \Big\downarrow R_{J_{2n}}$$

$$\mathbb{C}^n \xrightarrow{\;f_n\;} \mathbb{R}^{2n}$$

The composition of the three downward arrows on the left equals $R_{iAi} = R_{-A}$, so the composition of the three downward arrows on the right must equal $R_{\rho(-A)} = R_{-B}$. Therefore:

$$R_{-B} = R_{J_{2n}BJ_{2n}}.$$

It follows that $-B = J_{2n}BJ_{2n}$. Since $J_{2n}^2 = -I$, this implies that $B \cdot J_{2n} = J_{2n} \cdot B$.

The other direction is similar and is left to the reader. $\qquad\square$

2. Quaternionic matrices as complex matrices

The results in this section are analogous to results from the previous section, so we discuss them only briefly. The main idea is to think of elements of $M_n(\mathbb{H})$ as transformations of $\mathbb{C}^{2n}$ or $\mathbb{R}^{4n}$.

There is a natural bijection $g_n : \mathbb{H}^n \to \mathbb{C}^{2n}$ defined as

$$g_n(z_1 + w_1\mathbf{j}, z_2 + w_2\mathbf{j}, ..., z_n + w_n\mathbf{j}) := (z_1, w_1, z_2, w_2, ..., z_n, w_n).$$

Our goal is to define an injective map

$$\Psi_n : M_n(\mathbb{H}) \to M_{2n}(\mathbb{C})$$

such that the following diagram commutes for all $A \in M_n(\mathbb{H})$:

(2.2)
$$
\begin{array}{ccc}
\mathbb{H}^n & \xrightarrow{\;g_n\;} & \mathbb{C}^{2n} \\
{\scriptstyle R_A}\downarrow & & \downarrow{\scriptstyle R_{\Psi_n(A)}} \\
\mathbb{H}^n & \xrightarrow{\;g_n\;} & \mathbb{C}^{2n}
\end{array}
$$

The solution when $n = 1$ is:

$$\Psi_1(z + w\mathbf{j}) := \begin{pmatrix} z & w \\ -\overline{w} & \overline{z} \end{pmatrix},$$

where complex conjugation is denoted as $\overline{a + b\mathbf{i}} := a - b\mathbf{i}$. An alternative way to express Ψ_1 is:

$$\Psi_1(a + b\mathbf{i} + c\mathbf{j} + d\mathbf{k}) = \begin{pmatrix} a + b\mathbf{i} & c + d\mathbf{i} \\ -c + d\mathbf{i} & a - b\mathbf{i} \end{pmatrix}.$$

For $n > 1$, define Ψ_n in terms of Ψ_1 exactly the way ρ_n was defined in terms of ρ_1. For example,

$$\Psi_2 \begin{pmatrix} a_{11} + b_{11}\mathbf{i} + c_{11}\mathbf{j} + d_{11}\mathbf{k} & a_{12} + b_{12}\mathbf{i} + c_{12}\mathbf{j} + d_{12}\mathbf{k} \\ a_{21} + b_{21}\mathbf{i} + c_{21}\mathbf{j} + d_{21}\mathbf{k} & a_{22} + b_{22}\mathbf{i} + c_{22}\mathbf{j} + d_{22}\mathbf{k} \end{pmatrix}$$

$$= \begin{pmatrix} a_{11} + b_{11}\mathbf{i} & c_{11} + d_{11}\mathbf{i} & a_{12} + b_{12}\mathbf{i} & c_{12} + d_{12}\mathbf{i} \\ -c_{11} + d_{11}\mathbf{i} & a_{11} - b_{11}\mathbf{i} & -c_{12} + d_{12}\mathbf{i} & a_{12} - b_{12}\mathbf{i} \\ a_{21} + b_{21}\mathbf{i} & c_{21} + d_{21}\mathbf{i} & a_{22} + b_{22}\mathbf{i} & c_{22} + d_{22}\mathbf{i} \\ -c_{21} + d_{21}\mathbf{i} & a_{21} - b_{21}\mathbf{i} & -c_{22} + d_{22}\mathbf{i} & a_{22} - b_{22}\mathbf{i} \end{pmatrix}.$$

Matrices of $M_{2n}(\mathbb{C})$ in the image of Ψ_n are called <u>quaternionic-linear</u> complex matrices.

Proposition 2.6. *For all $\lambda \in \mathbb{R}$ and $A, B \in M_n(\mathbb{H})$,*

   (1) $\Psi_n(\lambda \cdot A) = \lambda \cdot \Psi_n(A)$.

   (2) $\Psi_n(A + B) = \Psi_n(A) + \Psi_n(B)$.

   (3) $\Psi_n(A \cdot B) = \Psi_n(A) \cdot \Psi_n(B)$.

Further, $B \in M_{2n}(\mathbb{C})$ is quaternionic-linear if and only if $g_n^{-1} \circ R_B \circ g_n : \mathbb{H}^n \to \mathbb{H}^n$ is an $\mathbb{H}$-linear transformation:

$$
\begin{array}{ccc}
\mathbb{H}^n & \xrightarrow{\;g_n\;} & \mathbb{C}^{2n} \\
& & \downarrow{\scriptstyle R_B} \\
\mathbb{H}^n & \xleftarrow{\;g_n^{-1}\;} & \mathbb{C}^{2n}
\end{array}
$$

Putting it together, we have injective maps $\rho_n : M_n(\mathbb{C}) \to M_{2n}(\mathbb{R})$ and $\Psi_n : M_n(\mathbb{H}) \to M_{2n}(\mathbb{C})$ such that the following commutes for all $A \in M_n(\mathbb{H})$:

$$
\begin{array}{ccccc}
\mathbb{H}^n & \xrightarrow{\;f_n\;} & \mathbb{C}^{2n} & \xrightarrow{\;g_{2n}\;} & \mathbb{R}^{4n} \\
\downarrow{\scriptstyle R_A} & & \downarrow{\scriptstyle R_{\Psi_n(A)}} & & \downarrow{\scriptstyle R_{(\rho_{2n} \circ \Psi_n)(A)}} \\
\mathbb{H}^n & \xrightarrow{\;f_n\;} & \mathbb{C}^{2n} & \xrightarrow{\;g_{2n}\;} & \mathbb{R}^{4n}
\end{array}
$$

Matrices of $M_{4n}(\mathbb{R})$ in the image of $(\rho_{2n} \circ \Psi_n) : M_n(\mathbb{H}) \to M_{4n}(\mathbb{R})$ are called <u>quaternionic-linear</u> real matrices.

Proposition 2.7. *The following are equivalent for $B \in M_{4n}(\mathbb{R})$.*

   (1) *B is quaternionic-linear.*

   (2) *B commutes with both $\mathcal{I}_{4n}$ and $\mathcal{J}_{4n}$.*

   (3) *$(f_n^{-1} \circ g_{2n}^{-1} \circ R_B \circ g_{2n} \circ f_n) : \mathbb{H}^n \to \mathbb{H}^n$ is $\mathbb{H}$-linear.*

$$
\begin{array}{ccccc}
\mathbb{H}^n & \xrightarrow{\;f_n\;} & \mathbb{C}^{2n} & \xrightarrow{\;g_{2n}\;} & \mathbb{R}^{4n} \\
& & & & \downarrow{\scriptstyle R_B} \\
\mathbb{H}^n & \xleftarrow{\;f_n^{-1}\;} & \mathbb{C}^{2n} & \xleftarrow{\;g_{2n}^{-1}\;} & \mathbb{R}^{4n}
\end{array}
$$

Here $\mathcal{I}_{4n}$ and $\mathcal{J}_{4n}$ are defined as the matrices which make these diagrams commute:

$$
\begin{array}{ccc}
\mathbb{H}^n & \xrightarrow{(g_{2n}\circ f_n)} & \mathbb{R}^{4n} \\
\downarrow \text{(scalar mult. i)} & & \downarrow R_{\mathcal{I}_{4n}} \\
\mathbb{H}^n & \xrightarrow{(g_{2n}\circ f_n)} & \mathbb{R}^{4n}
\end{array}
\qquad
\begin{array}{ccc}
\mathbb{H}^n & \xrightarrow{(g_{2n}\circ f_n)} & \mathbb{R}^{4n} \\
\downarrow \text{(scalar mult. j)} & & \downarrow R_{\mathcal{J}_{4n}} \\
\mathbb{H}^n & \xrightarrow{(g_{2n}\circ f_n)} & \mathbb{R}^{4n}
\end{array}
$$

"Scalar mult. **i**" means *left* scalar multiplication by **i**, and similarly for **j**. The analogy with Section 1 is imperfect, since $\mathcal{I}_{4n}$ and $\mathcal{J}_{4n}$ do not equal $(\rho_{2n} \circ \Psi_n)(\mathbf{i}I)$ and $(\rho_{2n} \circ \Psi_n)(\mathbf{j}I)$ (why?). The correct choice for $\mathcal{I}_4$ and $\mathcal{J}_4$ is easily seen to be:

$$
\mathcal{I}_4 = \begin{pmatrix} 0 & 1 & 0 & 0 \\ -1 & 0 & 0 & 0 \\ 0 & 0 & 0 & 1 \\ 0 & 0 & -1 & 0 \end{pmatrix}
\qquad
\mathcal{J}_4 = \begin{pmatrix} 0 & 0 & 1 & 0 \\ 0 & 0 & 0 & -1 \\ -1 & 0 & 0 & 0 \\ 0 & 1 & 0 & 0 \end{pmatrix}.
$$

The correct choice for $\mathcal{I}_{4n}$ (respectively $\mathcal{J}_{4n}$) has block-form with blocks of $\mathcal{I}_4$ (respectively $\mathcal{J}_4$) along the diagonal.

3. Restricting to the general linear groups

Proposition 2.8. *The image under ρ_n or Ψ_n of an invertible matrix is an invertible matrix.*

Proof. Let $A \in M_n(\mathbb{C})$. Then,

$$
\begin{aligned}
A \in GL_n(\mathbb{C}) \quad &\Longleftrightarrow \quad R_A : \mathbb{C}^n \to \mathbb{C}^n \text{ is bijective} \\
&\Longleftrightarrow \quad R_{\rho_n(A)} : \mathbb{R}^{2n} \to \mathbb{R}^{2n} \text{ is bijective} \\
&\Longleftrightarrow \quad \rho_n(A) \in GL_{2n}(\mathbb{R}).
\end{aligned}
$$

The argument for Ψ_n is similar. $\qquad\qquad\square$

Because of this proposition, we can restrict ρ_n and Ψ_n to maps between the general linear groups:

$$
\rho_n : GL_n(\mathbb{C}) \to GL_{2n}(\mathbb{R}),
$$
$$
\Psi_n : GL_n(\mathbb{H}) \to GL_{2n}(\mathbb{C}).
$$

By part (3) of Propositions 2.2 and 2.6, these maps are injective homomorphisms between the general linear groups. Theorem 2.1 is an immediate consequence of the existence of these injective homomorphisms.

Subsequent chapters contain many uses for the homomorphisms ρ_n and Ψ_n. As a first application, we now use Ψ_n to define the determinant of a quaternionic matrix. It turns out that there is no good way to define a quaternionic-valued determinant function on $M_n(\mathbb{H})$ (compare with Exercise 1.5). We will settle for a complex-valued determinant, namely, the composition

$$\det \circ \Psi_n : M_n(\mathbb{H}) \to \mathbb{C}.$$

For $A \in M_n(\mathbb{H})$ we will write $\det(A)$ to mean $\det(\Psi_n(A))$. It is obvious that $\det(I) = 1$ and $\det(A \cdot B) = \det(A) \cdot \det(B)$ for all $A, B \in M_n(\mathbb{H})$. Also, Proposition 1.15 extends to the $\mathbb{K} = \mathbb{H}$ case:

Proposition 2.9. $GL_n(\mathbb{H}) = \{A \in M_n(\mathbb{H}) \mid \det(A) \neq 0\}$.

Proof. Let $A \in M_n(\mathbb{H})$. As in the proof of Proposition 2.8, we have $A \in GL_n(\mathbb{H})$ if and only if $\Psi_n(A) \in GL_{2n}(\mathbb{C})$, which is equivalent to $\det(\Psi_n(A)) \neq 0$. $\square$

So now for all $K \in \{\mathbb{R}, \mathbb{C}, \mathbb{H}\}$, one can characterize the noninvertible matrices $A \in M_n(\mathbb{K})$ as those which satisfy $\det(A) = 0$, which is a polynomial equation in the entries of A.

The determinant of a quaternionic matrix is defined to be a complex number; surprisingly, it is always a real number:

Proposition 2.10. For all $A \in M_n(\mathbb{H})$, $\det(A) \in \mathbb{R}$.

The proof would take us too far afield from our topic, so we refer the reader to [**8**].

4. Exercises

Ex. 2.1. Prove that definition of ρ_n in the text makes diagram 2.1 commute.

Ex. 2.2. Prove Proposition 2.4.

Ex. 2.3. Prove Proposition 2.6.

Ex. 2.4. Prove Proposition 2.7.

Ex. 2.5. Prove that for any $A \in GL_1(\mathbb{H})$, $\det(A) \in \mathbb{R}$.

Ex. 2.6. Prove that $SL_n(\mathbb{H}) := \{A \in GL_n(\mathbb{H}) \mid \det(A) = 1\}$ is a subgroup. Describe a natural bijection between elements of $SL_1(\mathbb{H})$ and points of the 3-dimensional sphere S^3.

Ex. 2.7. Consider the following alternative way to define the function $f_n : \mathbb{C}^n \to \mathbb{R}^{2n}$:

$$f_n(a_1 + b_1 \mathbf{i}, ..., a_n + b_n \mathbf{i}) := (a_1, ..., a_n, b_1, ..., b_n).$$

Using this definition, how must ρ_n be defined so that diagram 2.1 commutes? How must J_{2n} be defined so that Proposition 2.5 is true?

Ex. 2.8. Is it possible to find a matrix $J \in M_{2n}(\mathbb{C})$ such that the following diagram commutes?

$$
\begin{array}{ccc}
\mathbb{H}^n & \xrightarrow{\;g_n\;} & \mathbb{C}^{2n} \\
{\scriptstyle(\text{scalar mult. by } \mathbf{j})}\Big\downarrow & & \Big\downarrow{\scriptstyle R_J} \\
\mathbb{H}^n & \xrightarrow{\;g_n\;} & \mathbb{C}^{2n}
\end{array}
$$

Ex. 2.9. Show that the image $\rho_n(M_n(\mathbb{C})) \subset M_{2n}(\mathbb{R})$ is a real vector subspace. What is its dimension?

Ex. 2.10. Are the matrices $\mathcal{I}_{4n}$ and $\mathcal{J}_{4n}$ defined in Proposition 2.7 quaternionic-linear?

Ex. 2.11. Is part (1) of Proposition 2.6 true when $\lambda \in \mathbb{C}$?

Chapter 3

The orthogonal groups

In this chapter, we define and study what are probably the most important subgroups of the general linear groups. These are denoted $O(n)$, $SO(n)$, $U(n)$, $SU(n)$ and $Sp(n)$. In particular, the group $SO(3)$, which was previously described as the "positions of a globe," now receives a more rigorous definition. We will continue to study these groups throughout the remainder of the book.

1. The standard inner product on $\mathbb{K}^n$

The conjugate and norm of an element $q \in \mathbb{K}$ are defined as:

(1) If $q \in \mathbb{R}$, then $\overline{q} := q$ and $|q|$ means the absolute value of q.

(2) If $q = a + b\mathbf{i} \in \mathbb{C}$, then $\overline{q} := a - b\mathbf{i}$ and $|q| := \sqrt{a^2 + b^2}$.

(3) If $q = a + b\mathbf{i} + c\mathbf{j} + d\mathbf{k} \in \mathbb{H}$, then $\overline{q} := a - b\mathbf{i} - c\mathbf{j} - d\mathbf{k}$ and $|q| := \sqrt{a^2 + b^2 + c^2 + d^2}$.

In all cases, it is a quick calculation to verify that for $q, q_1, q_2 \in \mathbb{K}$:

$$(3.1) \qquad \overline{q_1 \cdot q_2} = \overline{q}_2 \cdot \overline{q}_1.$$

$$(3.2) \qquad q \cdot \overline{q} = \overline{q} \cdot q = |q|^2.$$

These two equalities together imply that:

$$(3.3) \qquad |q_1 \cdot q_2| = |q_1| \cdot |q_2|.$$

Definition 3.1. *The* <u>*standard inner product on*</u> $\mathbb{K}^n$ *is the function from* $\mathbb{K}^n \times \mathbb{K}^n$ *to* $\mathbb{K}$ *defined by:*

$$\langle(x_1, x_2, ..., x_n), (y_1, y_2, ..., y_n)\rangle_\mathbb{K} := x_1 \cdot \overline{y}_1 + x_2 \cdot \overline{y}_2 + \cdots + x_n \cdot \overline{y}_n.$$

It follows from Equation 3.2 that for all $X \in \mathbb{K}^n$, $\langle X, X \rangle_\mathbb{K}$ is a real number that is ≥ 0 and equal to zero only when $X = (0, ..., 0)$. This allows us to define:

Definition 3.2. *The* <u>*standard norm on*</u> $\mathbb{K}^n$ *is the function from* $\mathbb{K}^n$ *to the nonnegative real numbers defined by:*

$$|X|_\mathbb{K} = \sqrt{\langle X, X \rangle_\mathbb{K}}.$$

We will omit the $\mathbb{K}$-subscripts whenever there is no ambiguity.

Proposition 3.3. *For all* $X, Y, Z \in \mathbb{K}^n$ *and* $\lambda \in \mathbb{K}$,

(1) $\langle X, Y + Z \rangle = \langle X, Y \rangle + \langle X, Z \rangle$,

(2) $\langle X + Y, Z \rangle = \langle X, Z \rangle + \langle Y, Z \rangle$,

(3) $\langle \lambda X, Y \rangle = \lambda \langle X, Y \rangle$ *and* $\langle X, \lambda Y \rangle = \langle X, Y \rangle \overline{\lambda}$,

(4) $\overline{\langle X, Y \rangle} = \langle Y, X \rangle$.

Definition 3.4.

- *Vectors* $X, Y \in \mathbb{K}^n$ *are called* <u>*orthogonal*</u> *if* $\langle X, Y \rangle = 0$.

- *A basis* $\{X_1, ..., X_n\}$ *of* $\mathbb{K}^n$ *is called* <u>*orthonormal*</u> *if* $\langle X_i, X_j \rangle$ *equals 1 when* $i = j$ *and equals zero when* $i \neq j$ *(that is, the vectors have norm 1 and are mutually orthogonal).*

- *The* <u>*standard orthonormal basis*</u> *of* $\mathbb{K}^n$ *is:*

$$e_1 = (1, 0, ..., 0), \ e_2 = (0, 1, 0, ..., 0), ..., e_n = (0, ..., 0, 1).$$

When $\mathbb{K} = \mathbb{R}$, the standard inner product is the familiar "dot product", described geometrically in terms of the angle θ between $X, Y \in \mathbb{R}^n$:

$$(3.4) \qquad \langle X, Y \rangle_\mathbb{R} = |X|_\mathbb{R}|Y|_\mathbb{R} \cos \theta.$$

When $\mathbb{K} = \mathbb{C}$, the standard inner product is also called the <u>hermitian</u> inner product. Since the hermitian inner product of two vectors $X, Y \in \mathbb{C}^n$ is a complex number, we should separately interpret the geometric meanings of its real and imaginary parts. The cleanest such interpretation is in terms of the identification

$$f = f_n : \mathbb{C}^n \to \mathbb{R}^{2n}$$

from the previous chapter. It is easy to verify that for all $X, Y \in \mathbb{C}^n$,

$$(3.5) \qquad \langle X, Y \rangle_\mathbb{C} = \langle f(X), f(Y) \rangle_\mathbb{R} + \mathbf{i} \langle f(X), f(\mathbf{i}Y) \rangle_\mathbb{R},$$
$$(3.6) \qquad |X|_\mathbb{C} = |f(X)|_\mathbb{R}.$$

If $X, Y \in \mathbb{C}^n$ are orthogonal, then two things are true:

$$\langle f(X), f(Y) \rangle_\mathbb{R} = 0 \quad \text{and} \quad \langle f(X), f(\mathbf{i}Y) \rangle_\mathbb{R} = 0.$$

This observation leads to:

Proposition 3.5. $\{X_1, ..., X_n\} \in \mathbb{C}^n$ *is an orthonormal basis if and only if* $\{f(X_1), f(\mathbf{i}X_1), ..., f(X_n), f(\mathbf{i}X_n)\}$ *is an orthonormal basis of* $\mathbb{R}^{2n}$.

When $\mathbb{K} = \mathbb{H}$, the standard inner product is also called the symplectic inner product. For $X, Y \in \mathbb{H}^n$, the 1, $\mathbf{i}$, $\mathbf{j}$ and $\mathbf{k}$ components of $\langle X, Y \rangle_\mathbb{H}$ are best interpreted geometrically in terms of the identification $h = f_{2n} \circ g_n : \mathbb{H}^n \to \mathbb{R}^{4n}$.

$$\langle X, Y \rangle_\mathbb{H} = \langle h(X), h(Y) \rangle_\mathbb{R} + \mathbf{i} \langle h(X), h(\mathbf{i}Y) \rangle_\mathbb{R}$$
$$+ \mathbf{j} \langle h(X), h(\mathbf{j}Y) \rangle_\mathbb{R} + \mathbf{k} \langle h(X), h(\mathbf{k}Y) \rangle_\mathbb{R}.$$
$$|X|_\mathbb{H} = |h(X)|_\mathbb{R}.$$

Proposition 3.6. $\{X_1, ..., X_n\} \in \mathbb{H}^n$ *is an orthonormal basis if and only if the following is an orthonormal basis of* $\mathbb{R}^{4n}$:

$$\{h(X_1), h(\mathbf{i}X_1), h(\mathbf{j}X_1), h(\mathbf{k}X_1), ..., h(X_n), h(\mathbf{i}X_n), h(\mathbf{j}X_n), h(\mathbf{k}X_n)\}.$$

The following inequality follows from Equation 3.4 when $\mathbb{K} = \mathbb{R}$:

Proposition 3.7 (Schwarz inequality). *For all* $X, Y \in \mathbb{K}^n$,

$$|\langle X, Y \rangle| \leq |X| \cdot |Y|.$$

Proof. Let $X, Y \in \mathbb{K}^n$. Let $\alpha := \langle X, Y \rangle$. Assume that $X \neq 0$ (otherwise the proposition is trivial). For all $\lambda \in \mathbb{K}$, we have:

$$
\begin{aligned}
0 \;\leq\; |\lambda X + Y|^2 &= \langle \lambda X + Y, \lambda X + Y \rangle \\
&= \lambda \langle X, X \rangle \overline{\lambda} + \lambda \langle X, Y \rangle + \langle Y, X \rangle \overline{\lambda} + \langle Y, Y \rangle \\
&= |\lambda|^2 |X|^2 + \lambda \langle X, Y \rangle + \overline{\lambda \langle X, Y \rangle} + |Y|^2 \\
&= |\lambda|^2 |X|^2 + 2\mathrm{Re}(\lambda \alpha) + |Y|^2.
\end{aligned}
$$

Choosing $\lambda = -\overline{\alpha}/|X|^2$ gives:

$$
0 \leq |\alpha|^2/|X|^2 - 2|\alpha|^2/|X|^2 + |Y|^2,
$$

which proves that $|\alpha| \leq |X| \cdot |Y|$ as desired. $\square$

2. Several characterizations of the orthogonal groups

Definition 3.8. *The orthogonal group over $\mathbb{K}$,*

$$
\mathcal{O}_n(\mathbb{K}) := \{ A \in GL_n(\mathbb{K}) \mid \langle XA, YA \rangle = \langle X, Y \rangle \text{ for all } X, Y \in \mathbb{K}^n \},
$$

... is denoted $O(n)$ and called the orthogonal group for $\mathbb{K} = \mathbb{R}$.

... is denoted $U(n)$ and called the unitary group for $\mathbb{K} = \mathbb{C}$.

... is denoted $Sp(n)$ and called the symplectic group for $\mathbb{K} = \mathbb{H}$.

It is straightforward to see that $\mathcal{O}_n(\mathbb{K})$ is a subgroup of $GL_n(\mathbb{K})$. Its elements are called orthogonal, unitary or symplectic matrices. To describe their form, it is useful to denote the conjugate-transpose of $A \in M_n(\mathbb{K})$ as $A^* := (\overline{A})^T$, where $\overline{A}$ means the matrix obtained by conjugating all of the entries of A.

Proposition 3.9. *For $A \in GL_n(\mathbb{K})$ the following are equivalent.*

(1) $A \in \mathcal{O}_n(\mathbb{K})$.

(2) R_A *preserves orthonormal bases; i.e., if $\{X_1, ..., X_n\}$ is an orthonormal basis of $\mathbb{K}^n$, then so is $\{R_A(X_1), ..., R_A(X_n)\}$.*

(3) *The rows of A form an orthonormal basis of $\mathbb{K}^n$.*

(4) $A \cdot A^* = I$.

Proof. $(1) \implies (2)$ is obvious. $(2) \implies (3)$ because the rows of A equal $\{R_A(e_1), ..., R_A(e_n)\}$. To see that $(3) \iff (4)$, notice that:

$$
\begin{aligned}
(A \cdot A^*)_{ij} &= (\text{row } i \text{ of } A) \cdot (\text{column } j \text{ of } A^*) \\
&= (\text{row } i \text{ of } A) \cdot (\text{row } j \text{ of } \overline{A})^T \\
&= \langle (\text{row } i \text{ of } A), (\text{row } j \text{ of } A) \rangle.
\end{aligned}
$$

Finally, we prove that $(3) \implies (1)$. If the rows of A are orthonormal, then for all $X = (x_1, ..., x_2), Y = (y_1, ..., y_n) \in \mathbb{K}^n$,

$$
\begin{aligned}
\langle R_A(X), & R_A(Y) \rangle \\
&= \left\langle \sum_{l=1}^{n} x_l(\text{row } l \text{ of } A), \sum_{s=1}^{n} y_s(\text{row } s \text{ of } A) \right\rangle \\
&= \sum_{l,s=1}^{n} x_l \langle (\text{row } l \text{ of } A), (\text{row } s \text{ of } A) \rangle \overline{y}_s \\
&= x_1 \overline{y}_1 + \cdots + x_n \overline{y}_n = \langle X, Y \rangle.
\end{aligned}
$$

$\square$

Geometrically, $O(n)$ is the group of matrices A for which the linear transformation $R_A : \mathbb{R}^n \to \mathbb{R}^n$ preserves dot products of vectors, and hence also norms of vectors. Such transformations should be visualized as "rigid motions" of $\mathbb{R}^n$ (we will be more precise about this in Section 5). The geometric meanings of $U(n)$ and $Sp(n)$ are best described in terms $O(n)$ by considering the homomorphisms from the previous chapter.

Proposition 3.10.

(1) $\rho_n(U(n)) = O(2n) \cap \rho_n(GL_n(\mathbb{C}))$.

(2) $\Psi_n(Sp(n)) = U(2n) \cap \Psi_n(GL_n(\mathbb{H}))$.

(3) $(\rho_{2n} \circ \Psi_n)(Sp(n)) = O(4n) \cap (\rho_{2n} \circ \Psi_n)(GL_n(\mathbb{H}))$.

Since $U(n)$ is isomorphic to its image, $\rho_n(U(n))$, part (1) says that $U(n)$ is isomorphic to the group of complex-linear real orthogonal matrices. In other words, $U(n)$ is isomorphic to the group of rigid motions of $\mathbb{R}^{2n}$ which preserve the standard complex structure. Similarly, part (3) says that $Sp(n)$ is isomorphic to the group of quaternionic-linear real orthogonal matrices.

Proof. We prove only (1), since (2) is similar and (3) follows from (1) and (2). The most straightforward idea is to use Equation 3.5. A quicker approach is to first notice that for all $A \in M_n(\mathbb{C})$,

$$\rho_n(A^*) = \rho_n(A)^*.$$

If $A \in GL_n(\mathbb{C})$, then $\rho_n(A) \cdot \rho_n(A)^* = \rho_n(A) \cdot \rho_n(A^*) = \rho_n(A \cdot A^*)$, which shows that $A \in U(n)$ if and only if $\rho_n(A) \in O(2n)$. □

We said that $\mathcal{O}_n(\mathbb{K})$ is the group of matrices A for which R_A preserves inner products of vectors, and hence also norms of vectors. The next result says that if R_A preserves norms, then it automatically preserves inner products.

Proposition 3.11.

$$\mathcal{O}_n(\mathbb{K}) = \{A \in GL_n(\mathbb{K}) \mid |R_A(X)| = |X| \text{ for all } X \in \mathbb{K}^n\}.$$

Proof. To prove the case $\mathbb{K} = \mathbb{R}$, we show that the inner product is completely determined by the norm. Solving the equation

$$|X + Y|_{\mathbb{R}}^2 = \langle X + Y, X + Y \rangle_{\mathbb{R}} = \langle X, X \rangle_{\mathbb{R}} + \langle Y, Y \rangle_{\mathbb{R}} + 2\langle X, Y \rangle_{\mathbb{R}}$$

for $\langle X, Y \rangle_{\mathbb{R}}$ gives:

$$\langle X, Y \rangle_{\mathbb{R}} = 1/2(|X + Y|_{\mathbb{R}}^2 - |X|_{\mathbb{R}}^2 - |Y|_{\mathbb{R}}^2).$$

So if R_A preserves norms, then it also preserves inner products.

The above argument doesn't work for $\mathbb{K} \in \{\mathbb{C}, \mathbb{H}\}$ (why not?). Instead, we prove the case $\mathbb{K} = \mathbb{C}$ as a consequence of the real case. Suppose $A \in GL_n(\mathbb{C})$ is such that $R_A : \mathbb{C}^n \to \mathbb{C}^n$ is norm-preserving. Then $R_{\rho_n(A)} : \mathbb{R}^{2n} \to \mathbb{R}^{2n}$ also preserves norms, since for all $X \in \mathbb{C}^n$,

$$|R_{\rho_n(A)}(f_n(X))|_{\mathbb{R}} = |f_n(R_A(X))|_{\mathbb{R}} = |R_A(X)|_{\mathbb{C}} = |X|_{\mathbb{C}} = |f_n(X)|_{\mathbb{R}}.$$

Therefore $\rho_n(A) \in O(n)$, which using Proposition 3.10 implies that $A \in U(n)$.

The $\mathbb{K} = \mathbb{H}$ case is proven from the real case in a similar fashion. □

3. The special orthogonal groups

In this section, we define important subgroups of the orthogonal groups, beginning with the observation that:

Proposition 3.12. *If* $A \in \mathcal{O}_n(\mathbb{K})$, *then* $|\det(A)| = 1$.

Proof. Since $A \cdot A^* = I$,

$$1 = \det(A \cdot A^*) = \det(A) \cdot \det(A^*) = \det(A) \cdot \overline{\det(A)} = |\det(A)|^2.$$

We used the fact that $\det(A^*) = \overline{\det(A)}$, which should be verified first for $\mathbb{K} \in \{\mathbb{R}, \mathbb{C}\}$. The quaternionic case follows from the complex case because for quaternionic matrices, $\det(A)$ means $\det(\Psi_n(A))$, and $\Psi_n(A^*) = \Psi_n(A)^*$. $\qquad\square$

The interpretation of Proposition 3.12 depends on $\mathbb{K}$:

- If $A \in O(n)$, then $\det(A) = \pm 1$.
- If $A \in U(n)$, then $\det(A) = e^{i\theta}$ for some $\theta \in [0, 2\pi)$.
- If $A \in Sp(n)$, then Proposition 2.10 implies $\det(A) = \pm 1$. We will see later that $\det(A) = 1$.

The subgroup

$$SO(n) := \{A \in O(n) \mid \det(A) = 1\}$$

is called the special orthogonal group. The subgroup

$$SU(n) := \{A \in U(n) \mid \det(A) = 1\}$$

is called the special unitary group. Both are clearly subgroups of the general linear group and in fact of the special linear group:

$$SL_n(\mathbb{K}) := \{A \in GL_n(\mathbb{K}) \mid \det(A) = 1\}.$$

Notice that $SO(n)$ comprises the orthogonal matrices whose determinants are one of two possibilities, while $SU(n)$ comprises the unitary matrices whose determinants are one of a circle's worth of possibilities. We will see later that the relationship of $SO(n)$ to $O(n)$ is very different from $SU(n)$ to $U(n)$.

4. Low dimensional orthogonal groups

In this section, we explicitly describe $\mathcal{O}_n(\mathbb{K})$ for small values of n. First, $O(1) = \{(1), (-1)\}$ and $SO(1) = \{(1)\}$ are isomorphic to the unique groups with 2 and 1 elements respectively.

Next, if $A \in O(2)$, then its two rows form an orthonormal basis of $\mathbb{R}^2$. Its first row is an arbitrary unit-length vector of $\mathbb{R}^2$, which can be written as $(\cos\theta, \sin\theta)$ for some θ. The second row is unit-length and orthogonal to the first, which leaves two choices: $(-\sin\theta, \cos\theta)$ or $(\sin\theta, -\cos\theta)$. For the first choice, $\det(A) = 1$, and for the second, $\det(A) = -1$. So we learn:

$$(3.7) \qquad SO(2) = \left\{ \begin{pmatrix} \cos\theta & \sin\theta \\ -\sin\theta & \cos\theta \end{pmatrix} \Big| \theta \in [0, 2\pi) \right\},$$

$$O(2) = SO(2) \cup \left\{ \begin{pmatrix} \cos\theta & \sin\theta \\ \sin\theta & -\cos\theta \end{pmatrix} \Big| \theta \in [0, 2\pi) \right\}.$$

$SO(2)$ is identified with the set of points on a circle; its group operation is addition of angles. $O(2)$ is a disjoint union of two circles. It is interesting that the disjoint union of two circles has a group operation.

Next, $SU(1) = \{(1)\}$ and $U(1) = \{(e^{i\theta}) \mid \theta \in [0, 2\pi)\}$, which is isomorphic to the circle-group $SO(2)$.

Next, $Sp(1) = \{(a + b\mathbf{i} + c\mathbf{j} + d\mathbf{k}) \mid a^2 + b^2 + c^2 + d^2 = 1\}$ is the group of unit-length quaternions, which is naturally identified with the three-dimensional sphere $S^3 \subset \mathbb{R}^4 \cong \mathbb{H}$. In fact, it follows from Equation 3.3 that the product of two unit-length quaternions is a unit-length quaternion. So we might have mentioned several pages ago the beautiful fact that *quaternionic multiplication provides a group operation on the three-dimensional sphere!* It turns out that S^0, S^1 and S^3 are the only spheres which are also groups.

We conclude this section by showing that $SU(2)$ is isomorphic to $Sp(1)$, and thus in some sense also has the shape of a 3-dimensional sphere.

Proposition 3.13. *$SU(2)$ is isomorphic to $Sp(1)$.*

Proof. First notice that

$$\Psi_1(Sp(1)) = \left\{ \begin{pmatrix} z & w \\ -\overline{w} & \overline{z} \end{pmatrix} \mid z, w \in \mathbb{C} \text{ such that } |z|^2 + |w|^2 = 1 \right\}$$

is a subgroup of $U(2)$ by Proposition 3.10, namely, the quaternionic-linear 2-by-2 unitary matrices. Calculating the determinant of such matrices shows that $\Psi_1(Sp(1)) \subset SU(2)$. We wish to prove that $\Psi_1(Sp(1)) = SU(2)$, so that Ψ_1 determines an isomorphism between $Sp(1)$ and $SU(2)$.

Let $A = \begin{pmatrix} z_1 & w_1 \\ w_2 & z_2 \end{pmatrix} \in SU(2)$. An easily verified formula for the inverse of a 2-by-2 matrix is: $A^{-1} = \frac{1}{\det(A)} \begin{pmatrix} z_2 & -w_1 \\ -w_2 & z_1 \end{pmatrix}$. In our case, $\det(A) = 1$ and $\begin{pmatrix} z_2 & -w_1 \\ -w_2 & z_1 \end{pmatrix} = A^{-1} = A^* = \begin{pmatrix} \overline{z}_1 & \overline{w}_2 \\ \overline{w}_1 & \overline{z}_2 \end{pmatrix}$, which tells us that $z_2 = \overline{z}_1$ and $w_2 = -\overline{w}_1$. It now follows that $SU(2) = \Psi_1(Sp(1))$. $\square$

5. Orthogonal matrices and isometries

In this section, we describe $O(n)$ geometrically as the group of isometries of $\mathbb{R}^n$ which fix the origin and discuss the difference between $SO(3)$ and $O(3)$.

The distance between points $X = (x_1, ..., x_n)$ and $Y = (y_1, ..., y_n)$ in $\mathbb{R}^n$ is measured as:

$$\text{dist}(X, Y) := |X - Y| = \sqrt{(x_1 - y_1)^2 + \cdots + (x_n - y_n)^2}.$$

A function $f : \mathbb{R}^n \to \mathbb{R}^n$ is called an <u>isometry</u> if for all $X, Y \in \mathbb{R}^n$, $\text{dist}(f(X), f(Y)) = \text{dist}(X, Y)$.

Proposition 3.14.

(1) If $A \in O(n)$ then $R_A : \mathbb{R}^n \to \mathbb{R}^n$ is an isometry.

(2) If $f : \mathbb{R}^n \to \mathbb{R}^n$ is an isometry with $f(0) = 0$, then $f = R_A$ for some $A \in O(n)$. In particular, f is linear.

Proof. For $A \in O(n)$ and $X, Y \in \mathbb{R}^n$,

$$
\begin{aligned}
\text{dist}(R_A(X), R_A(Y)) &= |R_A(X) - R_A(Y)| = |R_A(X - Y)| \\
&= |X - Y| = \text{dist}(X, Y),
\end{aligned}
$$

which proves that R_A is an isometry.

Conversely, suppose that $f : \mathbb{R}^n \to \mathbb{R}^n$ is an isometry for which $f(0) = 0$. For any $X \in \mathbb{R}^n$,

$$|f(X)| = \text{dist}(f(X), 0) = \text{dist}(f(X), f(0)) = \text{dist}(X, 0) = |X|,$$

which shows that f preserves norms. We showed in the proof of Proposition 3.11 that inner products are determined by norms, so f also preserves inner products; that is, for all $X, Y \in \mathbb{R}^n$,

$$\langle f(X), f(Y) \rangle = \langle X, Y \rangle.$$

Let A be the matrix whose ith row is $f(e_i)$, so $f(e_i) = R_A(e_i)$ for all $i = 1, ..., n$. Notice that $A \in O(n)$, since its rows are orthonormal. We will prove that $f = R_A$ (and thus that f is linear) by showing that $g := (R_A)^{-1} \circ f$ is the identity function. Notice that g is an isometry with $g(0) = 0$ (so g preserves norms and inner products, as above) and $g(e_i) = e_i$ for all $i = 1, ..., n$. Let $X \in \mathbb{R}^n$. Write $X = \sum a_i e_i$ and $g(X) = \sum b_i e_i$. Then,

$$b_i = \langle g(X), e_i \rangle = \langle g(X), g(e_i) \rangle = \langle X, e_i \rangle = a_i,$$

which proves $g(X) = X$, so g is the identity function. $\square$

$O(n)$ is the group of isometries of $\mathbb{R}^n$ which fix the origin and which therefore map the sphere $S^{n-1} \subset \mathbb{R}^n$ to itself. For example, elements of $O(3)$ represent functions from the "globe" $S^2 \subset \mathbb{R}^3$ to itself. We will see next that elements of $SO(3)$ represent real physical motions of the globe, which justifies our characterization of $SO(3)$ as the group of positions of a globe (Chapter 1, Section 1).

To understand the difference between $O(3)$ and $SO(3)$, we must discuss the <u>orientation of $\mathbb{R}^3$</u>. An ordered orthonormal basis of $\mathbb{R}^3$, like $\{X_1, X_2, X_3\}$, is called <u>right-handed</u> if $X_1 \times X_2 = X_3$, where "$\times$" denotes the vector cross product in $\mathbb{R}^3$. Visually, this means that if the fingers of your right hand are curled from X_1 towards X_2, then your thumb will point in the direction of X_3.

Proposition 3.15. *Let $A \in O(3)$. Then $A \in SO(3)$ if and only if the rows of A, $\{R_A(e_1), R_A(e_2), R_A(e_3)\}$, form a right-handed orthonormal basis.*

Proof. Let $R_A(e_1) = (a, b, c)$ and $R_A(e_2) = (d, e, f)$ denote the first two rows of A. The third row is unit-length and orthogonal to both, which leaves two choices:

$$R_A(e_3) = \pm(R_A(e_1) \times R_A(e_2)) = \pm(bf - ce, cd - af, ae - bd).$$

A quick calculation shows that the "+" choice gives $\det(A) > 0$, while the "-" choice gives $\det(A) < 0$. □

Elements of $SO(3)$ correspond to "physically performable motions" of a globe. This statement is imprecise, but in Chapter 9 we give it teeth by proving that every element of $SO(3)$ is a rotation through some angle about some single axis. An element of $O(3)$ with negative determinant turns the globe inside-out. For example, $R_{\text{diag}(-1,-1,-1)}$ maps each point of the globe to its antipode (its negative). This is not a physically performable motion.

6. The isometry group of Euclidean space

It is a straightforward exercise to show that

$$\text{Isom}(\mathbb{R}^n) := \{f : \mathbb{R}^n \to \mathbb{R}^n \mid f \text{ is an isometry}\}$$

is a group under composition of functions. The subgroup of isometries which fix the origin is isomorphic to $O(n)$. An isometry, f, that does not fix the origin is not linear, so cannot equal to R_A for any matrix A. In this case, let $V = f(0)$, so the function $X \mapsto f(X) - V$ is an isometry which fixes the origin and therefore equals R_A for some $A \in O(n)$. Therefore, an arbitrary isometry of $\mathbb{R}^n$ has the form

$$f(X) = R_A(X) + V$$

for some $A \in O(n)$ and $V \in \mathbb{R}^n$.

There is a clever trick for representing any isometry of $\mathbb{R}^n$ as a matrix, even ones which do not fix the origin. Graphics programmers use this trick to rotate *and translate* objects on the computer screen via matrices. We first describe the $n = 3$ case.

Let $A \in O(3)$ and $V = (v_1, v_2, v_3) \in \mathbb{R}^3$. We will represent the isometry $f(X) = R_A(X) + V$ by the matrix:

$$F := \begin{pmatrix} A & 0 \\ V & 1 \end{pmatrix} := \begin{pmatrix} A_{11} & A_{12} & A_{13} & 0 \\ A_{21} & A_{22} & A_{23} & 0 \\ A_{31} & A_{32} & A_{33} & 0 \\ v_1 & v_2 & v_3 & 1 \end{pmatrix} \in GL_4(\mathbb{R}).$$

Let $X = (x_1, x_2, x_3) \in \mathbb{R}^3$. Denote $(X, 1) = (x_1, x_2, x_3, 1) \in \mathbb{R}^4$. Notice that

$$(X, 1) \cdot F = (R_A(X) + V, 1) \in \mathbb{R}^4.$$

In this way, F represents f.

The composition of two isometries, like the ones represented by $F_1 = \begin{pmatrix} A_1 & 0 \\ V_1 & 1 \end{pmatrix}$ and $F_2 = \begin{pmatrix} A_2 & 0 \\ V_2 & 1 \end{pmatrix}$, is the isometry represented by the product:

$$\begin{pmatrix} A_1 & 0 \\ V_1 & 1 \end{pmatrix} \cdot \begin{pmatrix} A_2 & 0 \\ V_2 & 1 \end{pmatrix} = \begin{pmatrix} A_1 \cdot A_2 & 0 \\ R_{A_2}(V_1) + V_2 & 1 \end{pmatrix}.$$

Matrix multiplication is quite useful here. It allowed us to see immediately that the isometry $X \mapsto R_{A_1}(X) + V_1$ followed by the isometry $X \mapsto R_{A_2}(X) + V_2$ is the isometry $X \mapsto R_{(A_1 \cdot A_2)}(X) + R_{A_2}(V_1) + V_2$.

The above ideas also work for values of n other than 3. We conclude that $\mathrm{Isom}(\mathbb{R}^n)$ is isomorphic to the following subgroup of $GL_{n+1}(\mathbb{R})$:

$$\mathrm{Isom}(\mathbb{R}^n) \cong \left\{ \begin{pmatrix} A & 0 \\ V & 1 \end{pmatrix} \middle| A \in O(n) \text{ and } V \in \mathbb{R}^n \right\}.$$

Notice that the following subgroup of $\mathrm{Isom}(\mathbb{R}^n)$ is isomorphic to $(\mathbb{R}^n, +)$, which denotes $\mathbb{R}^n$ under the group-operation of vector-addition:

$$\mathrm{Trans}(\mathbb{R}^n) = \left\{ \begin{pmatrix} I & 0 \\ V & 1 \end{pmatrix} \middle| V \in \mathbb{R}^n \right\}.$$

This is the group of isometries of $\mathbb{R}^n$ which only translate and do not rotate. It is interesting that $(\mathbb{R}^n, +)$ is isomorphic to a matrix group!

7. Symmetry groups

The symmetry group of a subset $X \subset \mathbb{R}^n$ is the group of all isometries of $\mathbb{R}^n$ which carry X onto itself:

Definition 3.16. $Symm(X) := \{f \in Isom(\mathbb{R}^n) \mid f(X) = X\}$.

The statement "$f(X) = X$" means that each point of X is sent by f to a (possibly different) point of X.

For example, the symmetry group of the sphere $S^n \subset \mathbb{R}^{n+1}$ equals the group of isometries of $\mathbb{R}^{n+1}$ with no translational component, which is isomorphic to the orthogonal group:

$$\mathrm{Symm}(S^n) = \left\{ \begin{pmatrix} A & 0 \\ V & 1 \end{pmatrix} \middle| A \in O(n+1),\, V = (0, ..., 0) \right\} \cong O(n+1).$$

In an abstract algebra course, you probably met some important finite symmetry groups. For example, the symmetry group of a regular m-gon (triangle, square, pentagon, hexagon, etc.) centered at the origin in $\mathbb{R}^2$ is called the dihedral group of order $2m$, denoted D_m. The elements of D_m with determinant $+1$ are called rotations; they form a subgroup of index 2 which is isomorphic to the cyclic group $\mathbb{Z}_m$, of order m. The elements of D_m with determinant -1 are called flips.

The fact that half of the elements of D_m are rotations illustrates a general principal:

Definition 3.17. $Symm(X) = Symm^+(X) \cup Symm^-(X)$, where the sets
$$Symm^\pm(X) := \left\{ \begin{pmatrix} A & 0 \\ V & 1 \end{pmatrix} \middle| \det(A) = \pm 1 \right\}$$
are respectively called the "direct" and "indirect" symmetries of X.

Proposition 3.18. For any $X \subset \mathbb{R}^n$, $Symm^+(X) \subset Symm(X)$ is a subgroup with index 1 or 2.

The proof is left to the reader in Exercise 3.4. An example of a set $Y \subset \mathbb{R}^2$ whose direct symmetries have index 1 (meaning all symmetries are direct) is illustrated in Figure 1.

Symmetry groups of subsets of $\mathbb{R}^2$ are useful for studying objects which are essentially 2-dimensional, like snowflakes and certain

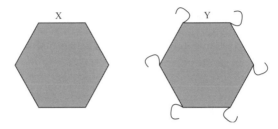

Figure 1. Symm$(X) = D_6$, while Symm$(Y) = \mathbb{Z}_6$.

crystal structures. Many subsets of $\mathbb{R}^2$, like the wallpaper tilings of $\mathbb{R}^2$ illustrated in some M.C. Escher prints, have infinite symmetry groups. Chapter 28 of [**5**] describes the classification of such infinite "wallpaper groups". Perhaps surprisingly, the only *finite* symmetry groups in dimension 2 are D_m and $\mathbb{Z}_m$. The following theorem is attributed to Leonardo da Vinci (1452-1519):

Proposition 3.19. *For* $X \subset \mathbb{R}^2$, *if* Symm(X) *is finite, then it is isomorphic to* D_m *or* $\mathbb{Z}_m$ *for some* m.

The proof involves two steps. First, when Symm(X) is finite, its elements must share a common fixed point, so it is isomorphic to a subgroup of $O(2)$. Second, D_m and $\mathbb{Z}_m$ are the only finite subgroups of $O(2)$.

Symmetry groups of subsets of $\mathbb{R}^3$ are even more interesting. In chemistry, the physical properties of a substance are intimately related to the symmetry groups of its molecules. In dimension 3, there are still very few possible finite symmetry groups:

Theorem 3.20. *For* $X \subset \mathbb{R}^3$, *if* Symm$^+(X)$ *is finite, then it is isomorphic to* D_m, $\mathbb{Z}_m$, A_4, S_4 *or* A_5.

Here, S_m denotes the group of permutations of a set with m elements, and $A_m \subset S_m$ denotes the subgroup of even permutations (called the <u>alternating group</u>). Like the $n = 2$ case, the proof involves verifying that all symmetries have a common fixed point and that the only finite subgroups of $SO(3)$ are D_m, $\mathbb{Z}_m$, A_4, S_4 and A_4.

The *regular solids* provide examples of sets whose direct symmetry groups equal A_4, S_4 and A_5. A <u>regular solid</u> (also called a "platonic solid" or a "regular polyhedra") is a polyhedra whose faces are mutually congruent regular polygons, at each of whose vertices the same number of edges meet. A famous classification theorem, attributed to Plato around 400 B.C., says that there are only five regular solids, pictured in Figure 2. The regular solids were once con-

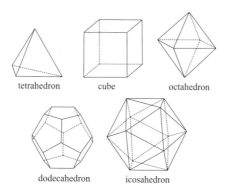

tetrahedron   cube   octahedron

dodecahedron   icosahedron

Figure 2. The five regular solids.

sidered to be sacred shapes, thought to represent fire, earth, air, the universe, and water. The fact that any other shape is "as symmetric" as one of these five (or is infinitely symmetric) enhances one's sense that the regular solids are of universal importance.

It turns out that A_4 is the direct symmetry group of a tetrahedron, S_4 is the direct symmetry group of a cube or an octahedron, and A_5 is the direct symmetry group of a dodecahedron or an icosahedron. See [**6**] for a complete calculation of these direct symmetry groups and a proof of Theorem 3.20. Since a cube has 6 faces, 12 edges, and 8 vertices, it may be surprising that its direct symmetry group is S_4. What does a cube have 4 of which get permuted by its direct symmetries? It has 4 diagonals (lines connecting antipodal pairs of vertices). This observation is the starting point of the calculation of its direct symmetry group.

8. Exercises

Ex. 3.1. Prove part (4) of Proposition 3.3.

Ex. 3.2. Prove equations 3.5 and 3.6.

Ex. 3.3. Prove Proposition 3.5.

Ex. 3.4. Prove Proposition 3.18.

Ex. 3.5. Let $A \in GL_n(\mathbb{K})$. Prove that $A \in \mathcal{O}_n(\mathbb{K})$ if and only if the columns of A are an orthonormal basis of $\mathbb{K}^n$.

Ex. 3.6.

(1) Show that for every $A \in O(2) - SO(2)$, $R_A : \mathbb{R}^2 \to \mathbb{R}^2$ is a flip about some line through the origin. How is this line determined by the angle of A (as in Equation 3.7)?

(2) Let $B = \begin{pmatrix} \cos\theta & \sin\theta \\ -\sin\theta & \cos\theta \end{pmatrix} \in SO(2)$. Assume that θ is not an integer multiple of π. Prove that B does not commute with any $A \in O(2) - SO(2)$. *Hint: Show that R_{AB} and R_{BA} act differently on the line in $\mathbb{R}^2$ about which A is a flip.*

Ex. 3.7. Describe the product of two arbitrary elements of $O(2)$ in terms of their angles (as in Equation 3.7).

Ex. 3.8. Let $A \in O(n)$ have determinant -1. Prove that:
$$O(n) = SO(n) \cup \{A \cdot B \mid B \in SO(n)\}.$$

Ex. 3.9. Define a map $f : O(n) \to SO(n) \times \{+1, -1\}$ as follows:
$$f(A) = (\det(A) \cdot A, \det A).$$

(1) If n is odd, prove that f is an isomorphism.

(2) Assume that n is odd and that $X \subset \mathbb{R}^n$ is symmetric about the origin, which means that $-p \in X$ if and only if $p \in X$. Also assume that $\text{Symm}(X) \subset O(n)$; in other words, X has no translational symmetries. Prove that $\text{Symm}(X)$ is isomorphic to $\text{Symm}^+(X) \times \{+1, -1\}$.
Comment: Four of the five regular solids are symmetric about the origin. The tetrahedron is not; its direct symmetry group is A_4 and its full symmetry group is S_4

(3) Prove that $O(2)$ is not isomorphic to $SO(2) \times \{+1, -1\}$. *Hint: How many elements of order two are there?*

Ex. 3.10. Prove that $\mathrm{Trans}(\mathbb{R}^n)$ is a normal subgroup of $\mathrm{Isom}(\mathbb{R}^n)$.

Ex. 3.11. Prove that the Affine group,

$$\mathrm{Aff}_n(\mathbb{K}) = \left\{ \begin{pmatrix} A & 0 \\ V & 1 \end{pmatrix} \Big| A \in GL_n(\mathbb{K}) \text{ and } V \in \mathbb{K}^n \right\}$$

is a subgroup of $GL_{n+1}(\mathbb{K})$. Any $F \in \mathrm{Aff}_n(\mathbb{K})$ can be identified with the function $f(X) = R_A(X) + V$ from $\mathbb{K}^n$ to $\mathbb{K}^n$ as in Section 6. Prove that f sends lines in $\mathbb{K}^n$ to lines in $\mathbb{K}^n$. A line in $\mathbb{K}^n$ means a set of the form $\{v_0 + v | v \in W\}$, where $v_0 \in \mathbb{K}^n$, and $W \subset \mathbb{K}^n$ is a 1-dimensional $\mathbb{K}$-subspace.

Ex. 3.12. Is $\mathrm{Aff}_1(\mathbb{R})$ abelian? Explain algebraically and visually.

Ex. 3.13. Let $A = \begin{pmatrix} 0 & 0 & 0 & 1 \\ 1 & 0 & 0 & 0 \\ 0 & 1 & 0 & 0 \\ 0 & 0 & 1 & 0 \end{pmatrix}$.

(1) Calculate $R_A(x, y, z, w)$.

(2) Describe a subgroup, H, of $O(4)$ which is isomorphic to S_4 ($S_4 = $ the group of permutations of a 4 elements set).

(3) Describe a subgroup, H, of $O(n)$ which is isomorphic to S_n. What is $H \cap SO(n)$?

(4) Prove that every finite group is isomorphic to a subgroup of $O(n)$ for some integer n. *Hint: Use Cayley's Theorem, found in any abstract algebra textbook.*

Ex. 3.14. Let $\mathfrak{g}$ be a $\mathbb{K}$-subspace of $\mathbb{K}^n$ with dimension d. Let $\mathcal{B} = \{X_1, ..., X_d\}$ be an orthonormal basis of $\mathfrak{g}$. Let $f : \mathfrak{g} \to \mathfrak{g}$ be $\mathbb{K}$-linear. Let $A \in M_n(\mathbb{K})$ represent f in the basis $\mathcal{B}$. Prove that the following are equivalent:

(1) $A \in \mathcal{O}_n(\mathbb{K})$.

(2) $\langle f(X), f(Y) \rangle = \langle X, Y \rangle$ for all $X, Y \in \mathfrak{g}$.

Show by example that this is false when $\mathcal{B}$ is not orthonormal.

Chapter 4

The topology of matrix groups

This text is about the subgroups of $GL_n(\mathbb{K})$. So far, we have considered such a subgroup, G, as a purely algebraic object. Geometric intuition has been relevant only because R_A is a *motion* of $\mathbb{K}^n$ for every $A \in G$.

We now begin to study G as a geometric object. Since

$$G \subset GL_n(\mathbb{K}) \subset M_n(\mathbb{K}) \cong \mathbb{K}^{n^2} \cong \begin{cases} \mathbb{R}^{n^2} & \text{if } \mathbb{K} = \mathbb{R} \\ \mathbb{R}^{2n^2} & \text{if } \mathbb{K} = \mathbb{C} \ , \\ \mathbb{R}^{4n^2} & \text{if } \mathbb{K} = \mathbb{H} \end{cases}$$

we can think of G as a subset of a Euclidean space, meaning $\mathbb{R}^m$ for some m. Many familiar subsets of Euclidean spaces, like the sphere $S^n \subset \mathbb{R}^{n+1}$, or the graphs of functions of several variables, have visualizable shapes. It makes sense to ask "what is the shape of G?" For example, we previously recognized the shape of $Sp(1)$ as the three-dimensional sphere S^3.

In this chapter, we learn some topology, which provides an ideal vocabulary for discussing the shape of a subset $G \subset \mathbb{R}^m$. Is it compact? path-connected? open? closed? We will define and briefly discuss these terms and apply them to subgroups of the general linear groups.

1. Open and closed sets and limit points

The natural <u>distance function</u> on $\mathbb{R}^m$ was defined in Section 3.5 as $\mathrm{dist}(X,Y) := |X - Y|$. Its most important property is:

Proposition 4.1 (The Triangle Inequality). *For all* $X, Y, Z \in \mathbb{R}^m$,

$$\mathrm{dist}(X, Z) \leq \mathrm{dist}(X, Y) + \mathrm{dist}(Y, Z).$$

Proof. For all $V, W \in \mathbb{R}^m$, the Schwarz inequality (Proposition 3.7) gives:

$$\begin{aligned}
|V + W|^2 &= |V|^2 + 2\langle V, W \rangle + |W|^2 \\
&\leq |V|^2 + 2|V| \cdot |W| + |W|^2 = (|V| + |W|)^2.
\end{aligned}$$

Thus, $|V + W| \leq |V| + |W|$. Applying this inequality to the vectors pictured in Figure 1 proves the triangle inequality.

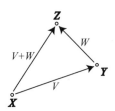

Figure 1. Proof of the triangle inequality.

$\square$

Our study of topology begins with precise language for discussing whether a subset of Euclidean space contains its boundary points. First, for $p \in \mathbb{R}^m$ and $r > 0$, we denote the <u>ball about p of radius r</u> as:

$$B(p, r) := \{q \in \mathbb{R}^m \mid \mathrm{dist}(p, q) < r\}.$$

In other words, $B(p, r)$ contains all points closer than a distance r from p.

Definition 4.2. *A point* $p \in \mathbb{R}^m$ *is called a* <u>*boundary point*</u> *of a subset* $S \subset \mathbb{R}^m$ *if for all* $r > 0$, *the ball* $B(p, r)$ <u>*contains at least one point*</u> *in* S *and at least one point not in* S. *The collection of all boundary points of* S *is called the* <u>*boundary*</u> *of* S.

Sometimes, but not always, boundary points of S are contained in S. For example, consider the "open upper half-plane"

$$H := \{(x, y) \in \mathbb{R}^2 \mid y > 0\},$$

and the "closed upper half-plane"

$$\overline{H} := \{(x, y) \in \mathbb{R}^2 \mid y \geq 0\}.$$

The x-axis, $\{(x, 0) \in \mathbb{R}^2\}$, is the boundary of H and also of $\overline{H}$. So H contains none of its boundary points, while $\overline{H}$ contains all of its boundary points. This distinction is so central we introduce vocabulary for it:

Definition 4.3. *Let $S \subset \mathbb{R}^m$ be a subset.*

   (1) *S is called <u>open</u> if it contains none of its boundary points.*

   (2) *S is called <u>closed</u> if it contains all of its boundary points.*

In the previous example, H is open, while $\overline{H}$ is closed. If part of the x-axis is adjoined to H (say the positive part), the result is neither closed nor open, since it contains some of its boundary points but not all of them.

A set $S \subset \mathbb{R}^m$ and its complement $S^c := \{p \in \mathbb{R}^m \mid p \notin S\}$ clearly have the same boundary. If S contains none of these common boundary points, then S^c must contain all of them, and vice-versa. So we learn that:

Proposition 4.4. *A set $S \subset \mathbb{R}^m$ is closed if and only if its complement, S^c, is open.*

The following provides a useful alternative definition of "open":

Proposition 4.5. *A set $S \subset \mathbb{R}^m$ is open if and only if for all $p \in S$, there exists $r > 0$ such that $B(p, r) \subset S$.*

Proof. If S is not open, then it contains at least one of its boundary points, and no ball about such a boundary point is contained in S. Conversely, suppose that there is a point $p \in S$ such that no ball about p is contained in S. Then p is a boundary point of S, so S is not open. $\qquad\square$

The proposition says that if you live in an open set, then so do all of your sufficiently close neighbors. How close is sufficient depends on how close you live from the boundary. For example, the set

$$S := (0, \infty) \subset \mathbb{R}$$

is open because for any $x \in S$, the ball $B(x, x/2) = (x/2, 3x/2)$ lies inside of S. When x is close to 0, the radius of this ball is small.

Figure 2. The set $(0, \infty) \subset \mathbb{R}$ is open because it contains a ball about each of its points.

Similarly, for any $p \in \mathbb{R}^m$ and any $r > 0$, the ball $B := B(p, r)$ is itself open because about any $q \in B$, the ball of radius $(r - \text{dist}(p, q))/2$ lies in B (by the triangle inequality).

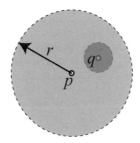

Figure 3. The set $B(p, r) \subset \mathbb{R}^m$ is open because it contains a ball about each of its points.

The collection of all open subsets of $\mathbb{R}^m$ is called the topology of $\mathbb{R}^m$. It is surprising how many important concepts are topological, that is, definable purely in terms of the topology of $\mathbb{R}^m$. For example, the notion of whether a subset is closed is topological. The distance between points of $\mathbb{R}^m$ is not topological. The notion of *convergence* is topological by the second definition below, although it may not initially seem so from the first:

Definition 4.6. *An infinite sequence* $\{p_1, p_2, ...\}$ *of points of* $\mathbb{R}^m$ *is said to <u>converge</u> to* $p \in \mathbb{R}^m$ *if either of the following equivalent conditions hold:*

(1) $\lim_{n \to \infty} dist(p, p_n) = 0$.

(2) *For every open set,* U, *containing* p, *there exists an integer* N *such that* $p_n \in U$ *for all* $n > N$.

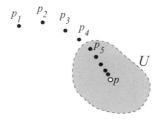

Figure 4. A convergent sequence is eventually inside of any open set containing its limit.

Definition 4.7. *A point* $p \in \mathbb{R}^m$ *is called a <u>limit point</u> of a subset* $S \subset \mathbb{R}^m$ *if there exists an infinite sequence of points of* S *which converges to* p.

Any point $p \in S$ is a limit point of S, as evidenced by the redundant infinite sequence $\{p, p, p, ...\}$. Any point of the boundary of S is a limit point of S as well (why?). In fact, the collection of limit points of S equals the union of S and the boundary of S. Therefore, *a set* $S \subset \mathbb{R}^m$ *is closed if and only if it contains all of its limit points,* since this is the same as requiring it to contain all of its boundary points.

It is possible to show that a sequence converges without knowing its limit just by showing that the terms get closer and closer to each other; more precisely,

Definition 4.8. *An infinite sequence of points* $\{p_1, p_2, ...\}$ *in* $\mathbb{R}^m$ *is called a <u>Cauchy sequence</u> if for every* $\epsilon > 0$ *there exists an integer* N *such that* $dist(p_i, p_j) < \epsilon$ *for all* $i, j > N$.

It is straightforward to prove that any convergent sequence is Cauchy. A fundamental property of Euclidean space is the converse:

Proposition 4.9. *Any Cauchy sequence in $\mathbb{R}^m$ converges to some point of $\mathbb{R}^m$.*

We end this chapter with an important relative notion of open and closed:

Definition 4.10. *Let $S \subset G \subset \mathbb{R}^m$ be subsets.*

(1) S *is called* <u>*open in G*</u> *if for all $p \in S$, $\exists r > 0$ such that*

$$\{q \in G \mid dist(p, q) < r\} \subset S.$$

(2) S *is called* <u>*closed in G*</u> *if $\{p \in G \mid p \notin S\}$ is open in G.*

For example, the interval $(0, 1)$ is open in $\mathbb{R}$, while the interval $[0, 1]$ is closed in $\mathbb{R}$. The interval $[0, 1)$ is neither open nor closed in $\mathbb{R}$, but is open in $[0, 2]$ and is closed in $(-1, 1)$.

The definition says that if you live in a set that's open in G, then so do all of your sufficiently close neighbors in G. An alternative definition is:

Proposition 4.11. *Let $S \subset G \subset \mathbb{R}^m$. Then S is open* (respectively closed) *in G if and only if $S = U \cap G$ for some open* (respectively closed) *subset U of $\mathbb{R}^m$.*

For example, if $G = S^2 = \{(x, y, z) \in \mathbb{R}^3 \mid x^2 + y^2 + z^2 = 1\}$, then the "open upper hemisphere" $\{(x, y, z) \in G \mid z > 0\}$ is open in G, because it is the intersection with G of the following open set:

$$\{(x, y, z) \in \mathbb{R}^3 \mid z > 0\}.$$

Our previous characterization of closed sets as those which contain all their limit points generalizes as follows:

Proposition 4.12. *Let $S \subset G \subset \mathbb{R}^m$. Then S is closed in G if and only if every $p \in G$ which is a limit point of S is contained in S.*

A set S is called <u>dense</u> in G if every point of G is a limit point of S. For example, the irrational numbers are dense in $\mathbb{R}$.

Let $p \in G \subset \mathbb{R}^m$. A <u>neighborhood</u> of p in G means a subset of G which is open in G and contains p. For example, $(1 - \epsilon, 1 + \epsilon)$ is a neighborhood of 1 in $(0, 2)$ for any $\epsilon \in (0, 1]$. Also, $[0, \epsilon)$ is a neighborhood of 0 in $[0, 1]$ for any $\epsilon \in (0, 1]$.

The collection of all subsets of G that are open in G is called the topology of G. In the remainder of this chapter, pay attention to which properties of a set G are topological, that is, definable in terms of only the topology of G. For example, the notion of a sequence of points of G converging to $p \in G$ is topological. Why? Because convergence means that the sequence is eventually inside of any neighborhood of p in $\mathbb{R}^m$; this is the same as being eventually inside of any neighborhood of p in G, which has only to do with the topology of G. The idea is to forget about the ambient $\mathbb{R}^m$ and regard G as an independent object with a topology and hence a notion of convergence.

2. Continuity

Let $G_1 \subset \mathbb{R}^{m_1}$ and $G_2 \subset \mathbb{R}^{m_2}$. A function $f : G_1 \to G_2$ is called *continuous* if it maps nearby points to nearby points; more precisely:

Definition 4.13. *A function $f : G_1 \to G_2$ is called <u>continuous</u> if for any infinite sequence $\{p_1, p_2, ...\}$ of points in G_1 which converges to a point $p \in G_1$, the sequence $\{f(p_1), f(p_2), ...\}$ converges to $f(p)$.*

For example, the "step function" $f : \mathbb{R} \to \mathbb{R}$ defined as

$$f(x) = \begin{cases} 0 & \text{if } x \leq 0 \\ 1 & \text{if } x > 0 \end{cases}$$

is not continuous. Why? Because the sequence

$$\{1/2, 1/3, 1/4, ...\}$$

in the domain of f converges to 0, but the images

$$\{f(1/2) = 1, f(1/3) = 1, f(1/4) = 1, ...\}$$

converge to 1 rather than to $f(0) = 0$.

Notice that f is continuous if and only if it is continuous when regarded as a function from G_1 to $\mathbb{R}^{m_2}$. It is nevertheless useful to forget about the ambient Euclidean spaces and regard G_1 and G_2 as independent objects. This vantage point leads to the following beautiful, although less intuitive, way to define continuity:

Proposition 4.14. *For $f : G_1 \to G_2$, the following are equivalent:*

(1) *f is continuous.*

(2) *For any set U that's open in G_2, $f^{-1}(U)$ is open in G_1.*

(3) *For any set U that's closed in G_2, $f^{-1}(U)$ is closed in G_1.*

Here, $f^{-1}(U)$ denotes the set $\{p \in G_1 \mid f(p) \in U\}$. The above step function fails this continuity test because

$$f^{-1}((-1/2, 1/2)) = (-\infty, 0],$$

which is not open.

It is now clear that continuity is a topological concept, since this alternative definition involved only the topologies of G_1 and G_2.

Familiar functions from $\mathbb{R}$ to $\mathbb{R}$, like polynomial, rational, trigonometric, exponential, and logarithmic functions, are all continuous on their domains. It is straightforward to prove that:

Proposition 4.15. *The composition of two continuous functions is continuous.*

We next wish to describe what it means for G_1 and G_2 to be "topologically the same". There should be a bijection between them which pairs open sets with open sets. More precisely,

Definition 4.16. *A function $f : G_1 \to G_2$ is called a <u>homeomorphism</u> if f is bijective and continuous and f^{-1} is continuous. If such a function exists, then G_1 and G_2 are said to be <u>homeomorphic</u>.*

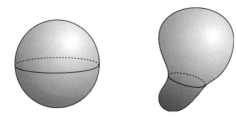

Figure 5. Homeomorphic sets.

Homeomorphic sets have the same "essential shape", like the two subsets of $\mathbb{R}^3$ pictured in Figure 5. The hypothesis that f^{-1} be continuous is necessary. To see this, consider the function $f : [0, 2\pi) \to S^1 \subset \mathbb{R}^2$ defined as $f(t) = (\cos t, \sin t)$. It is straightforward to check that f is continuous and bijective, but f^{-1} is not continuous (why not?). We will see in Section 4 that $[0, 2\pi)$ is not homeomorphic to S^1, since only the latter is compact.

3. Path-connected sets

Definition 4.17. *A subset $G \subset \mathbb{R}^m$ is called <u>path-connected</u> if for every pair $p, q \in G$, there exists a continuous function $f : [0, 1] \to G$ with $f(0) = p$ and $f(1) = q$.*

The terminology comes from visualizing the image of such an f as a "path" in G beginning at p and ending at q.

For example, the disk $A = \{(x, y) \in \mathbb{R}^2 \mid x^2 + y^2 < 1\}$ is path-connected, since any pair $p, q \in A$ can be connected by the straight line segment between them, explicitly parameterized as

$$f(t) := p + t(q - p).$$

But the disjoint union of two discs,

$$B = \{p \in \mathbb{R}^2 \mid \text{dist}(p, (-2, 0)) < 1 \text{ or } \text{dist}(p, (2, 0)) < 1\},$$

is not path-connected, because no continuous path exists between points in different disks (why not?).

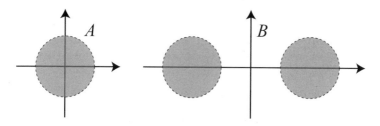

Figure 6. *A is path-connected, while B is not.*

In the non-path-connected example, the right disk is <u>clopen</u> (both open and closed) in B, and therefore so too is the left disk. In other words, B decomposes into the disjoint union of two subsets which are both clopen in B. Such a separation of a path-connected set is impossible:

Proposition 4.18. *A path-connected set $G \subset \mathbb{R}^m$ has no clopen subsets other than itself and the empty set.*

Proof. We first prove that the interval $[0, 1]$ has no clopen subsets other than itself and the empty set. Suppose $A \subset [0, 1]$ is another one. Let t denote the infimum of A. Since A is closed, $t \in A$. Since A is open, there exists $r > 0$ such that all points of $[0, 1]$ with distance $< r$ from t lie in A. This contradicts the fact that t is the infimum of A unless $t = 0$. Therefore, $0 \in A$. Since the complement A^c of A is also clopen, the same argument proves that $0 \in A^c$, which is impossible.

Next, let $G \subset \mathbb{R}^m$ be any path-connected set. Suppose that $A \subset G$ is a clopen subset. Suppose there exist points $p, q \in G$ such that $p \in A$ and $q \notin A$. Since G is path-connected, there exists a continous function $f : [0, 1] \to G$ with $f(0) = p$ and $f(1) = q$. Then $f^{-1}(A)$ is a clopen subset of $[0, 1]$ which contains 0 but not 1, contradicting the previous paragraph. $\qquad\square$

In practice, to prove that a property is true at all points in a path-connected set, it is often convenient to prove that the set of points where the property holds is non-empty, open, and closed.

Since continuity is a topological notion, so is path-connectedness. In particular,

Proposition 4.19. *If $G_1 \subset \mathbb{R}^{m_1}$ and $G_2 \subset \mathbb{R}^{m_2}$ are homeomorphic, then either both are path-connected or neither is path-connected.*

4. Compact sets

The notion of compactness is fundamental to topology. We begin with the most intuitive definition.

Definition 4.20. *A subset $G \subset \mathbb{R}^m$ is called <u>bounded</u> if $G \subset B(p, r)$ for some $p \in \mathbb{R}^m$ and some $r > 0$. Further, G is called <u>compact</u> if it is closed and bounded.*

Compact sets are those which contain their limit points and lie in a finite chunk of Euclidean space. Unfortunately, this definition is not topological, since "bounded" cannot be defined without referring to the distance function on $\mathbb{R}^m$. In particular, boundedness is not preserved by homeomorphisms, since the bounded set $(0, 1)$ is homeomorphic to the unbounded set $\mathbb{R}$. Nevertheless, compactness is a topological notion, as is shown by the following alternative definition:

Definition 4.21. *Let $G \subset \mathbb{R}^m$.*

(1) *An <u>open cover</u> of G is a collection, $\mathbb{O}$, of sets which are open in G, whose union equals G.*

(2) *G is called <u>compact</u> if every open cover, $\mathbb{O}$, of G has a finite subcover, meaning a finite sub-collection $\{U_1, ..., U_n\} \subset \mathbb{O}$ whose union equals G.*

The equivalence of our two definitions of compactness is called the <u>Heine-Borel Theorem</u>. The easy half of its proof goes like this: Suppose that G is not bounded. Then the collection

$$\{p \in G \mid \operatorname{dist}(0, p) < n\},$$

for $n = 1, 2, 3, ...$, is an open cover of G with no finite subcover. Next suppose that G is not closed, which means it is missing a limit point $q \in \mathbb{R}^m$. Then the collection $\{p \in G \mid \operatorname{dist}(p, q) > 1/n\}$, for $n = 1, 2, 3, ...$, is an open cover of G with no finite subcover.

The other half of the proof is substantially more difficult. We content ourselves with a few examples.

The open interval $(0, 1) \subset \mathbb{R}$ is not compact because it is not closed or because

$$\mathbb{O} = \{(0, 1/2), (0, 2/3), (0, 3/4), (0, 4/5)...\}$$

is an open cover of $(0, 1)$ which has no finite subcover.

The closed interval $[0, 1]$ is compact because it is closed and bounded. It is somewhat difficult to prove directly that every open cover of $[0, 1]$ has a finite subcover; attempting to do so will increase your appreciation of the Heine-Borel Theorem.

Since our second definition of compactness is topological, it is straightforward to prove that:

Proposition 4.22. *If $G_1 \subset \mathbb{R}^{m_1}$ and $G_2 \subset \mathbb{R}^{m_2}$ are homeomorphic, then either both are compact or neither is compact.*

There is a third useful characterization of compactness, which depends on the notion of *sub-convergence*.

Definition 4.23. *An infinite sequence of points $\{p_1, p_2, p_3, ...\}$ in $\mathbb{R}^m$ is said to* sub-converge *to $p \in \mathbb{R}^m$ if there is an infinite sub-sequence, $\{p_{i_1}, p_{i_2}, p_{i_3}, ...\}$ (with $i_1 < i_2 < i_3 < \cdots$) which converges to p.*

Proposition 4.24. *A subset $G \subset \mathbb{R}^m$ is compact if and only if every infinite sequence of points in G sub-converges to some $p \in G$.*

For example, the sequence $\{1/2, 2/3, 3/4, ...\}$ in $G = (0, 1)$ sub-converges only to $1 \notin G$, which gives another proof that $(0, 1)$ is not compact.

The next proposition says that the continuous image of a compact set is compact.

Proposition 4.25. *Let $G \subset \mathbb{R}^{m_1}$. Let $f : G \to \mathbb{R}^{m_2}$ be continuous. If G is compact, then the image $f(G)$ is compact.*

Proof. The function f is also continuous when regarded as a function from G to $f(G)$. Let $\mathbb{O}$ be an open cover of $f(G)$. Then $f^{-1}(U)$ is open in G for every $U \in \mathbb{O}$, so $f^{-1}(\mathbb{O}) := \{f^{-1}(U) \mid U \in \mathbb{O}\}$ is an open cover of G. Since G is compact, there exists a finite subcover $\{f^{-1}(U_1), ..., f^{-1}(U_n)\}$ of $f^{-1}(\mathbb{O})$. It is straightforward to check that $\{U_1, U_2, ..., U_n\}$ is a finite subcover of $\mathbb{O}$. $\square$

Corollary 4.26. *If $G \subset \mathbb{R}^m$ is compact and $f : G \to \mathbb{R}$ is continuous, then f attains is supremum and infimum.*

The conclusion that f attains is supremum means two things. First, the supremum of $f(G)$ is finite (because $f(G)$ is bounded). Second, there is a point $p \in G$ for which $f(p)$ equals this supremum (because $f(G)$ is closed).

5. Definition and examples of matrix groups

As mentioned earlier in this chapter, a subgroup $G \subset GL_n(\mathbb{K})$ can be considered a subset of Euclidean space, so we can ask whether it is open, closed, path-connected, compact, etc. The title of this book comes from:

Definition 4.27. *A matrix group is a subgroup $G \subset GL_n(\mathbb{K})$ which is closed in $GL_n(\mathbb{K})$.*

The "closed" hypothesis means that if a sequence of matrices in G has a limit in $GL_n(\mathbb{K})$, then that limit must lie in G. In other words, G contains all of its non-singular limit points.

We now verify that several previously introduced subgroups of $GL_n(\mathbb{K})$ are closed and are therefore matrix groups.

Proposition 4.28. *$\mathcal{O}_n(\mathbb{K})$, $SL_n(\mathbb{K})$, $SO(n)$ and $SU(n)$ are matrix groups.*

Proof. We must prove that each is closed in $GL_n(\mathbb{K})$. For $\mathcal{O}_n(\mathbb{K})$, define $f : M_n(\mathbb{K}) \to M_n(\mathbb{K})$ as $f(A) := A \cdot A^*$. This function f is continuous, because for each i, j, the $\mathbb{K}$-valued function

$$f_{ij}(A) := (A \cdot A^*)_{ij}$$

is continuous because it is a polynomial in the entries of A. The single-element set $\{I\} \subset M_n(\mathbb{K})$ is closed, so $\mathcal{O}_n(\mathbb{K}) = f^{-1}(\{I\})$ is closed in $M_n(\mathbb{K})$ and is therefore closed in $GL_n(\mathbb{K})$.

For $SL_n(\mathbb{K})$, we first prove the function $\det : M_n(\mathbb{K}) \to \mathbb{R}$ or $\mathbb{C}$ is continuous. When $\mathbb{K} \in \{\mathbb{R}, \mathbb{C}\}$, this is because $\det(A)$ is an n-degree polynomial in the entries of A by Equation 1.5. When $\mathbb{K} = \mathbb{H}$, this is because $\det(A)$ is shorthand for $\det(\Phi_n(A))$, and the composition of two continuous functions is continuous. Since the single-element set $\{1\}$ is closed, $SL_n(\mathbb{K}) = \det^{-1}(\{1\})$ is closed in $M_n(\mathbb{K})$ and therefore also in $GL_n(\mathbb{K})$.

For $SO(n)$ and $SU(n)$, notice that $SO(n) = O(n) \cap SL_n(\mathbb{R})$ and $SU(n) = U(n) \cap SL_n(\mathbb{C})$, and the intersection of two closed sets is closed. □

In the remainder of this book, we will emphasize compact matrix groups, so the following proposition is crucial:

Proposition 4.29. *Each of the groups $O(n)$, $SO(n)$, $U(n)$, $SU(n)$ and $Sp(n)$ is compact for any n.*

Proof. In proving above that these groups are closed in $GL_n(\mathbb{K})$, we actually proved the stronger fact that they are closed in the Euclidean space $M_n(\mathbb{K})$. So it remains to prove that these groups are bounded, which follows from the fact that each row of $A \in \mathcal{O}_n(\mathbb{K})$ is unit-length; see part (3) of Proposition 3.9. $\square$

In the exercises, you will verify that several other familiar matrix groups are non-compact, like $GL_n(\mathbb{K})$ for $n \geq 1$ and $SL_n(\mathbb{K})$ for $n \geq 2$.

Why did we define matrix groups to be closed in $GL_n(\mathbb{K})$? Because, as we will see later, non-closed subgroups are not necessarily manifolds. Exercises 4.23 and 4.24 exhibit the bad behavior of non-closed subgroups which underlies this fact. Nevertheless, the hypothesis that matrix groups are closed will not be used until Chapter 7. Until then, the facts we prove about matrix groups will also be true for non-closed subgroups of $GL_n(\mathbb{K})$.

6. Exercises

Ex. 4.1. Prove Proposition 4.11.

Ex. 4.2. Prove Proposition 4.12.

Ex. 4.3. Prove Proposition 4.14.

Ex. 4.4. Prove Proposition 4.15.

Ex. 4.5. Prove Proposition 4.19.

Ex. 4.6. Prove Proposition 4.22.

Ex. 4.7. Prove that $GL_n(\mathbb{K})$ is open in $M_n(\mathbb{K})$.

Ex. 4.8. Prove that $GL_n(\mathbb{K})$ in non-compact when $n \geq 1$. Prove that $SL_n(\mathbb{K})$ is non-compact when $n \geq 2$. What about $SL_1(\mathbb{K})$?

Ex. 4.9. Let G be a matrix group. Prove that a subgroup $H \subset G$ which is closed in G is itself a matrix group.

Ex. 4.10. Prove that $SO(n)$ and
$$O(n)^- := \{A \in O(n) \mid \det(A) = -1\}$$
are both clopen in $O(n)$.

Ex. 4.11. Prove that $\text{Aff}_n(\mathbb{K}) \subset GL_{n+1}(\mathbb{K})$ (defined in Exercise 3.11) is a matrix group. Show that $\text{Aff}_n(\mathbb{K})$ is NOT closed in $M_{n+1}(\mathbb{K})$. Is $\text{Aff}_n(\mathbb{K})$ compact?

Ex. 4.12. A matrix $A \in M_n(\mathbb{K})$ is called <u>upper triangular</u> if all entries below the diagonal are zero; i.e., $A_{ij} = 0$ for all $i < j$. Prove that the following is a matrix group:

$$UT_n(\mathbb{K}) = \{A \in GL_n(\mathbb{K}) \mid A \text{ is upper triangular}\}.$$

Show that $UT_n(\mathbb{K})$ is not closed in $M_n(\mathbb{K})$. Is $UT_n(\mathbb{K})$ compact?

Ex. 4.13. Prove that $\text{Isom}(\mathbb{R}^n)$ is a matrix group. Is is compact?

Ex. 4.14. Prove that $SO(3)$ is path-connected.

Ex. 4.15. Prove that $Sp(1)$ is path-connected.

Ex. 4.16. Prove that the image under a continuous function of a path-connected set is path-connected.

Ex. 4.17. We will prove later that $Sp(n)$ is path-connected. Assuming this, and using Propositions 2.10 and 3.12, prove that the determinant of any $A \in Sp(n)$ equals 1.

Ex. 4.18. Prove that $\mathcal{O}_n(\mathbb{K})$ is isomorphic to a subgroup of $\mathcal{O}_{n+1}(\mathbb{K})$.

Ex. 4.19. Prove that $U(n)$ is isomorphic to a subgroup of $SU(n+1)$.

Ex. 4.20. Let $G \subset GL_n(\mathbb{R})$ be a compact subgroup.

  (1) Prove that every element of G has determinant 1 or -1.
  (2) Must it be true that $G \subset O(n)$?
      Hint: Consider conjugates of $O(n)$.

Ex. 4.21. There are two natural functions from $SU(n) \times U(1)$ to $U(n)$. The first is $f_1(A, (\lambda)) := \lambda \cdot A$. The second is $f_2(A, (\lambda)) := $ the result of multiplying each entry of the first row of A times λ.

  (1) Prove that f_1 is an n-to-1 homomorphism.
  (2) Prove that f_2 is a homeomorphism but not a homomorphism.

Later we will prove that $U(n)$ is not isomorphic to $SU(n) \times U(1)$, even though they are homeomorphic.

Ex. 4.22. $SO(2)$ is a subgroup of $SL_2(\mathbb{R})$. Another is:

$$H = \left\{ \begin{pmatrix} a & b \\ 0 & a^{-1} \end{pmatrix} \in M_2(\mathbb{R}) \middle| a \neq 0 \right\}.$$

Prove that the function $f : SO(2) \times H \to SL_2(\mathbb{R})$ defined as $f(A, B) = A \cdot B$ is a homeomorphism, but not a homomorphism. This is a special case of the <u>polar decomposition</u> theorem, which states that $SL_n(\mathbb{R})$ is homeomorphic to $SO(n)$ times a Euclidean space.

Ex. 4.23. Let $\lambda \in \mathbb{R}$ be an irrational multiple of 2π. Define

$$G := \{(e^{\lambda t i}) | t \in \mathbb{Z}\} \subset U(1) \subset GL_1(\mathbb{C}).$$

Prove that G is a subgroup of $GL_1(\mathbb{C})$, but not a matrix group. Prove that G is dense in $U(1)$.

Ex. 4.24. Let $\lambda \in \mathbb{R}$ be an irrational multiple of 2π. Define

$$G = \left\{ \begin{pmatrix} e^{ti} & 0 \\ 0 & e^{\lambda t i} \end{pmatrix} \middle| t \in \mathbb{R} \right\} \subset \overline{G} = \left\{ \begin{pmatrix} e^{ti} & 0 \\ 0 & e^{si} \end{pmatrix} \middle| t, s \in \mathbb{R} \right\} \subset GL_2(\mathbb{C}).$$

(1) Prove that G and $\overline{G}$ are subgroups of $GL_2(\mathbb{C})$.

(2) Prove that G is dense in $\overline{G}$.

(3) Define $f : \mathbb{R} \to G$ as follows: $f(t) = \begin{pmatrix} e^{ti} & 0 \\ 0 & e^{\lambda t i} \end{pmatrix}$. Show that f is an isomorphism (with $\mathbb{R}$ considered a group under addition), but not a homeomorphism.

Ex. 4.25. Let $G \subset GL_n(\mathbb{R})$ denote the set of matrices whose determinants are integer powers of 2. Is G a matrix group?

Ex. 4.26. Prove or find a counterexample of each statement:

(1) If $X \subset \mathbb{R}^n$ is compact, then $\mathrm{Symm}(X)$ is compact.

(2) If $\mathrm{Symm}(X)$ is compact, then X is compact.

Chapter 5

Lie algebras

A matrix group $G \subset GL_n(\mathbb{K})$ is a subset of the Euclidean space $M_n(\mathbb{K})$, so we can discuss its tangent spaces.

Definition 5.1. *Let $G \subset \mathbb{R}^m$ be a subset, and let $p \in G$. The tangent space to G at p is:*

$$T_pG := \{\gamma'(0) \mid \gamma : (-\epsilon, \epsilon) \to G \text{ is differentiable with } \gamma(0) = p\}.$$

In other words, T_pG means the set of initial velocity vectors of differentiable paths though p in G. The term *differentiable* means that, when we consider γ as a path in $\mathbb{R}^m$, the m components of γ are differentiable functions from $(-\epsilon, \epsilon)$ to $\mathbb{R}$.

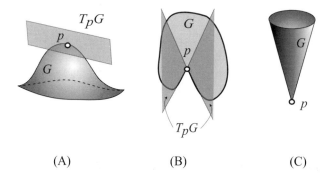

| (A) | (B) | (C) |

If $G \subset \mathbb{R}^3$ is the graph of a differentiable function of two variables, then T_pG is a 2-dimensional subspace of $\mathbb{R}^3$, as in Figure A (subspaces always pass though the origin; its translate to p is actually what is drawn). For a general subset $G \subset \mathbb{R}^m$, T_pG is not necessarily a subspace of $\mathbb{R}^m$. In Figure B, the tangent space is two sectors, while in Figure C, the tangent space is $\{0\}$.

Definition 5.2. *The Lie algebra of a matrix group $G \subset GL_n(\mathbb{K})$ is the tangent space to G at I. It is denoted $\mathfrak{g} := \mathfrak{g}(G) := T_IG$.*

In this chapter, we prove that $\mathfrak{g}$ is a subspace of the Euclidean space $M_n(\mathbb{K})$. This is our first evidence that matrix groups are "nice" sets (you should picture them like Figure A, not like B or C; we will make this precise when we prove that matrix groups are manifolds in Chapter 7). We also describe the Lie algebras of many familiar matrix groups.

The Lie algebra is an indispensable tool for studying a matrix group. It contains a surprising amount of information about the group, especially together with the Lie bracket operation, which we will discuss in Chapter 8. In much of the remainder of this book, we will learn about matrix groups by studying their Lie algebras.

1. The Lie algebra is a subspace

Let $G \subset GL_n(\mathbb{K}) \subset M_n(\mathbb{K})$ be a matrix group. At the beginning of Chapter 4, we described how $M_n(\mathbb{K})$ can be identified with a Euclidean space. For example, $M_2(\mathbb{C}) \cong \mathbb{R}^8$ via the identification:

$$\begin{pmatrix} a + b\mathbf{i} & c + d\mathbf{i} \\ e + f\mathbf{i} & g + h\mathbf{i} \end{pmatrix} \leftrightarrow (a, b, c, d, e, f, g, h).$$

This identification allows us to talk about tangent vectors to differentiable paths in $M_n(\mathbb{K})$. For example a differentiable path in $M_2(\mathbb{C})$ has the form:

$$\gamma(t) = \begin{pmatrix} a(t) + b(t)\mathbf{i} & c(t) + d(t)\mathbf{i} \\ e(t) + f(t)\mathbf{i} & g(t) + h(t)\mathbf{i} \end{pmatrix},$$

where $a(t)$ through $h(t)$ are differentiable functions. The derivative is:

$$\gamma'(t) = \begin{pmatrix} a'(t) + b'(t)\mathbf{i} & c'(t) + d'(t)\mathbf{i} \\ e'(t) + f'(t)\mathbf{i} & g'(t) + h'(t)\mathbf{i} \end{pmatrix}.$$

Matrix multiplication interacts with differentiation in the following way.

Proposition 5.3 (The product rule). *If $\gamma, \beta : (-\epsilon, \epsilon) \to M_n(\mathbb{K})$ are differentiable, then so is the product path $(\gamma \cdot \beta)(t) := \gamma(t) \cdot \beta(t)$, and*

$$(\gamma \cdot \beta)'(t) = \gamma(t) \cdot \beta'(t) + \gamma'(t) \cdot \beta(t).$$

Proof. When $n = 1$ and $\mathbb{K} = \mathbb{R}$, this is the familiar product rule from calculus. When $n = 1$ and $\mathbb{K} = \mathbb{C}$, we denote $\gamma(t) = a(t) + b(t)\mathbf{i}$ and $\beta(t) = c(t) + d(t)\mathbf{i}$. Omitting the t's to shorten notation, we have:

$$
\begin{aligned}
(\gamma \cdot \beta)' &= ((ac - bd) + (ad + bc)\mathbf{i})' \\
&= (ac' + a'c - bd' - b'd) + (ad' + a'd + bc' + b'c)\mathbf{i} \\
&= ((ac' - bd') + (ad' + bc')\mathbf{i}) + ((a'c - b'd) + (a'd + b'c)\mathbf{i} \\
&= \gamma \cdot \beta' + \gamma' \cdot \beta.
\end{aligned}
$$

When $n = 1$ and $\mathbb{K} = \mathbb{H}$, an analogous argument works. This completes the $n = 1$ case. For the general case, since

$$((\gamma \cdot \beta)(t))_{ij} = \sum_{l=1}^{n} \gamma(t)_{il} \cdot \beta(t)_{lj},$$

the derivative is:

$$
\begin{aligned}
((\gamma \cdot \beta)'(t))_{ij} &= \sum_{l=1}^{n} \gamma(t)_{il} \cdot \beta'(t)_{lj} + \gamma'(t)_{il} \cdot \beta(t)_{lj} \\
&= (\gamma(t) \cdot \beta'(t))_{ij} + (\gamma(t) \cdot \beta'(t))_{ij}.
\end{aligned}
$$

$\square$

If $\gamma : (-\epsilon, \epsilon) \to GL_n(\mathbb{K})$ is a differentiable path, so is the inverse path $t \mapsto \gamma(t)^{-1}$ (see Exercise 5.16). The product rule gives:

$$0 = \frac{d}{dt}\left(\gamma(t)\gamma(t)^{-1}\right) = \gamma'(t)\gamma(t)^{-1} + \gamma(t)\frac{d}{dt}\left(\gamma(t)^{-1}\right).$$

When $\gamma(0) = I$, the solution is particularly clean:

(5.1) $$\frac{d}{dt}\Big|_{t=0}\left(\gamma(t)^{-1}\right) = -\gamma'(0).$$

In other words, the inverse of a path through I goes through I in the opposite direction.

Another consequence of the product rule is the main result of this section:

Proposition 5.4. *The Lie algebra* $\mathfrak{g}$ *of a matrix group* $G \subset GL_n(\mathbb{K})$ *is a real subspace of* $M_n(\mathbb{K})$.

Proof. Let $\lambda \in \mathbb{R}$ and $A \in \mathfrak{g}$, which means that $A = \gamma'(0)$ for some differentiable path $\gamma(t)$ in G with $\gamma(0) = I$. The path $\sigma(t) := \gamma(\lambda \cdot t)$ has initial velocity vector $\sigma'(0) = \lambda \cdot A$, which proves that $\lambda \cdot A \in \mathfrak{g}$.

Next let $A, B \in \mathfrak{g}$, which means that $A = \gamma'(0)$ and $B = \beta'(0)$ for some differentiable paths γ, β in G with $\gamma(0) = \beta(0) = I$. The product path $\sigma(t) := \gamma(t) \cdot \beta(t)$ is differentiable and lies in G. By the product rule, $\sigma'(0) = A + B$, which shows that $A + B \in \mathfrak{g}$. $\qquad\square$

The fact that Lie algebras are vector spaces over $\mathbb{R}$ allows us to define an important measurement of the size of a matrix group:

Definition 5.5. *The* _dimension_ *of a matrix group* G *means the dimension of its Lie algebra.*

Even though $M_n(\mathbb{C}) \cong \mathbb{C}^{n^2}$ is a vector space over $\mathbb{C}$ (rather than just a vector space over $\mathbb{R}$), the Lie algebra of a complex matrix group $G \subset GL_n(\mathbb{C})$ is NOT necessarily a $\mathbb{C}$-subspace of $M_n(\mathbb{C})$. Similarly, the Lie algebra of a quaternionic matrix group need not be an $\mathbb{H}$-subspace of $M_n(\mathbb{H})$. The dimension of a matrix group always means the dimension of its Lie algebra regarded as a REAL vector space.

2. Some examples of Lie algebras

In this section, we describe the Lie algebras of three familiar matrix groups. Lie algebras are denoted in lower case; for example, $gl_n(\mathbb{K})$ denotes the Lie algebra of $GL_n(\mathbb{K})$.

Proposition 5.6. $gl_n(\mathbb{K}) = M_n(\mathbb{K})$. *In particular,*
$\dim(GL_n(\mathbb{R})) = n^2$, $\dim(GL_n(\mathbb{C})) = 2n^2$ *and* $\dim(GL_n(\mathbb{H})) = 4n^4$.

Proof. Let $A \in M_n(\mathbb{K})$. The path $\gamma(t) := I + t \cdot A$ in $M_n(\mathbb{K})$ satisfies $\gamma(0) = I$ and $\gamma'(0) = A$. Also, γ restricted to a sufficiently small interval $(-\epsilon, \epsilon)$ lies in $GL_n(\mathbb{K})$. To justify this, notice $\det(\gamma(0)) = 1$. Since the determinant function is continuous, $\det(\gamma(t))$ is close to 1 (and is therefore non-zero) for t close to 0. This demonstrates that $A \in gl_n(\mathbb{K})$. $\qquad\square$

The general linear groups are large; all matrices are tangent to paths in them. But matrices in the Lie algebras of other matrix groups have special forms.

Proposition 5.7. *The Lie algebra* $u(1)$ *of* $U(1)$ *equals span*$\{(\mathbf{i})\}$, *so* $\dim(U(1)) = 1$.

Proof. The path $\gamma(t) = (e^{\mathbf{i}t})$ in $U(1)$ satisfies $\gamma(0) = I$ and has $\gamma'(0) = (\mathbf{i})$, so $(\mathbf{i}) \in u(1)$. Therefore span$\{(\mathbf{i})\} \subset u(1)$. For the other inclusion, let $\gamma(t) = (a(t) + b(t)\mathbf{i})$ be a differentiable path in $U(1)$ with $\gamma(0) = I = (1)$. Since $|\gamma(t)|^2 = a(t)^2 + b(t)^2 = 1$, the value $a(0) = 1$ must be a local maximum of $a(t)$, so $a'(0) = 0$. Therefore $\gamma'(0) \in$ span$\{(\mathbf{i})\}$. □

A similar argument shows that $\dim(SO(2)) = 1$. We will see later that smoothly isomorphic matrix groups have the same dimension.

Proposition 5.8. *The Lie algebra of* $Sp(1)$ *is*

$$sp(1) = span\{(\mathbf{i}), (\mathbf{j}), (\mathbf{k})\},$$

so $\dim(Sp(1)) = 3$.

Proof. The path $\gamma_1(t) = (\cos(t) + \sin(t)\mathbf{i})$ in $Sp(1)$ satisfies $\gamma_1(0) = I$ and $\gamma_1'(0) = (\mathbf{i})$, so $\mathbf{i} \in sp(1)$. Similarly, $\gamma_2(t) = (\cos(t) + \sin(t)\mathbf{j})$ and $\gamma_3(t) = (\cos(t) + \sin(t)\mathbf{k})$ have initial velocities $\gamma_2'(0) = (\mathbf{j})$ and $\gamma_3'(0) = (\mathbf{k})$. So span$\{(\mathbf{i}), (\mathbf{j}), (\mathbf{k})\} \subset sp(1)$.

For the other inclusion, let $\gamma(t) = (a(t) + b(t)\mathbf{i} + c(t)\mathbf{j} + d(t)\mathbf{k})$ be a differentiable path in $Sp(1)$ with $\gamma(0) = I = (1)$. Since

$$|\gamma(t)|^2 = a(t)^2 + b(t)^2 + c(t)^2 + d(t)^2 = 1,$$

the value $a(1) = 1$ must be a local maximum of $a(t)$, so $a'(0) = 0$. Therefore $\gamma'(0) \in$ span$\{(\mathbf{i}), (\mathbf{j}), (\mathbf{k})\}$. □

In Figure 1, the circle group $U(1)$ and its Lie algebra are pictured on the left. The right image inaccurately represents $Sp(1)$ as $S^2 \subset \mathbb{R}^3$ rather than $S^3 \subset \mathbb{R}^4$, but is still a useful picture to keep in mind.

We end this section by describing the Lie algebras of the special linear groups.

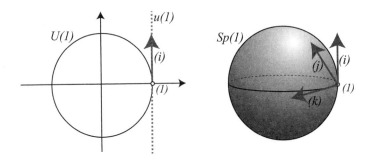

Figure 1. The Lie algebras of $U(1)$ and $Sp(1)$.

Theorem 5.9. *Let* $\mathbb{K} \in \{\mathbb{R}, \mathbb{C}\}$. *The Lie algebra* $sl_n(\mathbb{K})$ *of* $SL_n(\mathbb{K})$ *is:*

$$sl_n(\mathbb{K}) = \{A \in M_n(\mathbb{K}) \mid trace(A) = 0\}.$$

In particular, $\dim(SL_n(\mathbb{R})) = n^2 - 1$ *and* $\dim(SL_n(\mathbb{C})) = 2(n^2 - 1)$.

The proof relies on the important fact that the trace is the derivative of the determinant; more precisely,

Lemma 5.10. *Let* $\mathbb{K} \in \{\mathbb{R}, \mathbb{C}\}$. *If* $\gamma : (-\epsilon, \epsilon) \to M_n(\mathbb{K})$ *is differentiable and* $\gamma(0) = I$, *then*

$$\frac{d}{dt}\Big|_{t=0} \det(\gamma(t)) = trace(\gamma'(0)).$$

Proof. Using the notation of Equation 1.5,

$$\begin{aligned}
&\frac{d}{dt}\Big|_{t=0} \det(\gamma(t)) \\
&= \frac{d}{dt}\Big|_{t=0} \sum_{j=1}^{n} (-1)^{j+1} \cdot \gamma(t)_{1j} \cdot \det(\gamma(t)[1,j]) \\
&= \sum_{j=1}^{n} (-1)^{j+1} \Big(\gamma'(0)_{1j} \cdot \det(\gamma(0)[1,j]) \\
&\qquad\qquad + \gamma(0)_{1j} \cdot \frac{d}{dt}\Big|_{t=0} \det(\gamma(t)[1,j]) \Big) \\
&= \gamma'(0)_{11} + \frac{d}{dt}\Big|_{t=0} \det(\gamma(t)[1,1]) \qquad (\text{since } \gamma(0) = I).
\end{aligned}$$

Re-applying the above argument to compute $\frac{d}{dt}\big|_{t=0}\det(\gamma(t)[1,1])$ and repeating n times gives:

$$\frac{d}{dt}\bigg|_{t=0}\det(\gamma(t)) = \gamma'(0)_{11} + \gamma'(0)_{22} + \cdots + \gamma'(0)_{nn}.$$

$\square$

Proof of Theorem 5.9. If $\gamma : (-\epsilon, \epsilon) \to SL_n(\mathbb{K})$ is differentiable with $\gamma(0) = I$, the lemma implies that trace$(\gamma'(0)) = 0$. This proves that every matrix in $sl_n(\mathbb{K})$ has trace zero.

On the other hand, suppose $A \in M_n(\mathbb{K})$ has trace zero. The path $\gamma(t) := I + tA$ satisfies $\gamma(0) = I$ and $\gamma'(0) = A$, but this path is not in $SL_n(\mathbb{K})$. Define $\alpha(t)$ as the result of multiplying each entry in the first row of $\gamma(t)$ by $1/\det(\gamma(t))$. Notice that $\alpha(t)$ is a differentiable path in $SL_n(\mathbb{K})$ with $\alpha(0) = I$. Further, since trace$(A) = 0$, it is straightforward to show that $\alpha'(0) = A$ (Exercise 5.2). This proves that every trace-zero matrix is in $sl_n(\mathbb{K})$. An alternative proof is to choose $\alpha(t)$ to be a one-parameter group, which will be introduced in the next chapter. $\square$

3. Lie algebra vectors as vector fields

A <u>vector field</u> on $\mathbb{R}^m$ means a continuous function $F : \mathbb{R}^m \to \mathbb{R}^m$. By picturing $F(v)$ as a vector drawn at $v \in \mathbb{R}^m$, we think of a vector field as associating a vector to each point of $\mathbb{R}^m$.

If $A \in M_n(\mathbb{K})$, then $R_A : \mathbb{K}^n \to \mathbb{K}^n$ is a vector field on $\mathbb{K}^n$ ($= \mathbb{R}^n$, $\mathbb{R}^{2n}$ or $\mathbb{R}^{4n}$). The vector fields on $\mathbb{R}^2$ associated to the matrices $A = \begin{pmatrix} 0 & 1 \\ -1 & 0 \end{pmatrix}$ and $B = \begin{pmatrix} 1 & 0 \\ 0 & -1 \end{pmatrix}$ are shown in Figure 2.

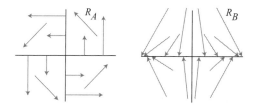

Figure 2. Vector fields on $\mathbb{R}^2$ associated to the matrices A and B.

Elements of $GL_n(\mathbb{K})$ are thought of as linear transformations of $\mathbb{K}^n$ (by the correspondence $A \leftrightarrow R_A$); therefore, a differentiable path $\gamma : (-\epsilon, \epsilon) \to GL_n(\mathbb{K})$ should be regarded as a *one-parameter family* of linear transformations of $\mathbb{K}^n$. How does this family act on a single vector $X \in \mathbb{K}^n$? To decide this, let $\sigma(t) := R_{\gamma(t)}(X)$, which is a differentiable path in $\mathbb{K}^n$. If $\gamma(0) = I$, then $\sigma(0) = X$. By the product rule (which holds also for non-square matrices),

$$\sigma'(0) = R_{\gamma'(0)}(X).$$

We can think of $R_{\gamma'(0)}$ as a vector field on $\mathbb{K}^n$ whose value at any $X \in \mathbb{K}^n$ tells the direction X is initially moved by the family of linear transformations corresponding to the path $\gamma(t)$. In this way, it is often useful to visualize an element $\gamma'(0)$ of the Lie algebra of a matrix group $G \subset GL_n(\mathbb{K})$ as represented by the vector field $R_{\gamma'(0)}$ on $\mathbb{K}^n$.

For example, consider the path $\gamma(t) = \begin{pmatrix} \cos t & \sin t \\ -\sin t & \cos t \end{pmatrix}$ in $SO(2)$. Its initial tangent vector, $A = \gamma'(0) = \begin{pmatrix} 0 & 1 \\ -1 & 0 \end{pmatrix}$, lies in the Lie algebra $so(2)$ of $SO(2)$. In fact, $so(2) = \text{span}\{A\}$. The vector field R_A in Figure 2 illustrates how this family of rotations initially moves individual points of $\mathbb{R}^2$. The rotating action of the family $\gamma(t)$ of transformations is clearly manifested in the vector field R_A.

Next look at the graph of R_B in Figure 2. Can you see from this graph why B is not in the Lie algebra of $so(2)$? If $\gamma(t)$ is a path in $GL_2(\mathbb{R})$ with $\gamma(0) = I$ and $\gamma'(0) = B$, then for small t, $R_{\gamma(t)} : \mathbb{R}^2 \to \mathbb{R}^2$ does not preserve norms. Which $X \in \mathbb{R}^2$ have initially increasing norms, and which are initially shrinking?

The vector field R_A has an important visual property that R_B lacks: the vector at any point is perpendicular to that point. By the above visual reasoning, we expect that for general $A \in M_n(\mathbb{R})$, if the vector field R_A lacks this property, then A could not lie in the Lie algebra $so(n)$ of $SO(n)$. We could promote this visual reasoning to a careful proof without too much work (Exercise 5.11), but instead we use a cleaner, purely algebraic proof in the next section.

4. The Lie algebras of the orthogonal groups

The set $o_n(\mathbb{K}) = \{A \in M_n(\mathbb{K}) \mid A + A^* = 0\}$

- ... is denoted $so(n)$ and called the skew-symmetric matrices if $\mathbb{K} = \mathbb{R}$.
- ... is denoted $u(n)$ and called the skew-hermitian matrices if $\mathbb{K} = \mathbb{C}$.
- ... is denoted $sp(n)$ and called the skew-symplectic matrices if $\mathbb{K} = \mathbb{H}$.

We wish to prove that $o_n(\mathbb{K})$ is the Lie algebra of $\mathcal{O}_n(\mathbb{K})$. The condition $A = -A^*$ means that $A_{ij} = -\overline{A}_{ji}$ for all $i, j = 1...n$. So, the entries below the diagonal are determined by the entries above, and the diagonal entries are purely imaginary (which means zero if $\mathbb{K} = \mathbb{R}$). For example,

$$(5.2)\ u(2) = \left\{ \begin{pmatrix} a\mathbf{i} & b + c\mathbf{i} \\ -b + c\mathbf{i} & d\mathbf{i} \end{pmatrix} \Big| a, b, c, d \in \mathbb{R} \right\}$$

$$= \operatorname{span}\left\{ \begin{pmatrix} 0 & 1 \\ -1 & 0 \end{pmatrix}, \begin{pmatrix} 0 & \mathbf{i} \\ \mathbf{i} & 0 \end{pmatrix}, \begin{pmatrix} \mathbf{i} & 0 \\ 0 & 0 \end{pmatrix}, \begin{pmatrix} 0 & 0 \\ 0 & \mathbf{i} \end{pmatrix} \right\},$$

which is a 4 dimensional $\mathbb{R}$-subspace of $M_2(\mathbb{C})$, but not a $\mathbb{C}$-subspace. Also,

$$sp(2) = \left\{ \begin{pmatrix} a_1\mathbf{i} + b_1\mathbf{j} + c_1\mathbf{k} & x + y\mathbf{i} + z\mathbf{j} + w\mathbf{k} \\ -x + y\mathbf{i} + z\mathbf{j} + w\mathbf{k} & a_2\mathbf{i} + b_2\mathbf{j} + c_2\mathbf{k} \end{pmatrix} \Big| \begin{matrix} a_i, b_i, c_i, \\ x, y, z, w \end{matrix} \in \mathbb{R} \right\},$$

and

$$so(3) = \left\{ \begin{pmatrix} 0 & a & b \\ -a & 0 & c \\ -b & -c & 0 \end{pmatrix} \Big| a, b, c \in \mathbb{R} \right\}.$$

If $A \in so(n)$, then the vector field R_A on $\mathbb{R}^n$ has the property discussed in the previous section: the vector at any point is perpendicular to that point. This follows from (3) below:

Lemma 5.11. *For $A \in M_n(\mathbb{K})$, the following are equivalent:*

(1) $A \in o_n(\mathbb{K})$.

(2) $\langle R_A(X), Y \rangle = -\langle X, R_A(Y) \rangle$ *for all $X, Y \in \mathbb{K}^n$.*

(3) *(assuming $\mathbb{K} = \mathbb{R}$) $\langle R_A(X), X \rangle = 0$ for all $X \in \mathbb{R}^n$.*

Proof. To see that $(1) \implies (2)$, notice that for all $i, j = 1...n$,

$$\langle R_A(e_i), e_j \rangle = A_{ij} = -\overline{A}_{ji} = -\overline{\langle R_A(e_j), e_i \rangle} = -\langle e_i, R_A(e_j) \rangle.$$

This verifies (2) for X, Y chosen from the standard orthonormal basis of $\mathbb{K}^n$. It is straightforward to extend linearly to arbitrary $X, Y \in \mathbb{K}^n$. The proof that $(2) \implies (1)$ is similar.

Now assume that $\mathbb{K} = \mathbb{R}$. In this case, $(2) \implies (3)$ by letting $X = Y$. To see that $(3) \implies (2)$, notice that:

$$
\begin{aligned}
0 &= \langle R_A(X + Y), X + Y \rangle \\
&= \langle R_A(X), X \rangle + \langle R_A(Y), Y \rangle + \langle R_A(X), Y \rangle + \langle R_A(Y), X \rangle \\
&= 0 + 0 + \langle R_A(X), Y \rangle + \langle R_A(Y), X \rangle.
\end{aligned}
$$

$\square$

Theorem 5.12. *The Lie algebra of* $\mathcal{O}_n(\mathbb{K})$ *equals* $o_n(\mathbb{K})$.

Proof. Suppose $\gamma : (-\epsilon, \epsilon) \to \mathcal{O}_n(\mathbb{K})$ is differentiable with $\gamma(0) = I$. Using the product rule to differentiate both sides of

$$\gamma(t) \cdot \gamma(t)^* = I$$

gives $\gamma'(0) + \gamma'(0)^* = 0$, so $\gamma'(0) \in o_n(\mathbb{K})$. This demonstrates that $\mathfrak{g}(\mathcal{O}_n(\mathbb{K})) \subset o_n(\mathbb{K})$.

Proving the other inclusion means explicitly constructing a path in $\mathcal{O}_n(\mathbb{K})$ in the direction of any $A \in o_n(\mathbb{K})$. It is simpler and sufficient to do so for all A in a basis of $o_n(k)$.

The natural basis of $so(n) = o_n(\mathbb{R})$ is the set

$$\{E_{ij} - E_{ji} | 1 \leq i < j \leq n\},$$

where E_{ij} denotes the matrix with ij-entry 1 and other entries zero. For example,

$$
\begin{aligned}
so(3) &= \mathrm{span}\{E_{12} - E_{21}, E_{13} - E_{31}, E_{23} - E_{32}\} \\
&= \mathrm{span}\left\{ \begin{pmatrix} 0 & 1 & 0 \\ -1 & 0 & 0 \\ 0 & 0 & 0 \end{pmatrix}, \begin{pmatrix} 0 & 0 & 1 \\ 0 & 0 & 0 \\ -1 & 0 & 0 \end{pmatrix}, \begin{pmatrix} 0 & 0 & 0 \\ 0 & 0 & 1 \\ 0 & -1 & 0 \end{pmatrix} \right\}.
\end{aligned}
$$

The path

$$\gamma_{ij}(t) := I + (\sin t)E_{ij} - (\sin t)E_{ji} + (-1 + \cos t)(E_{ii} + E_{jj})$$

lies in $SO(n)$, has $\gamma_{ij}(0) = I$ and has initial direction

$$\gamma'_{ij}(0) = E_{ij} - E_{ji}.$$

$R_{\gamma_{ij}(t)} : \mathbb{R}^n \to \mathbb{R}^n$ rotates the subspace $\text{span}\{e_i, e_j\}$ by an angle t and does nothing to the other basis vectors. For example, the path

$$\gamma_{13}(t) = \begin{pmatrix} \cos t & 0 & \sin t \\ 0 & 1 & 0 \\ -\sin t & 0 & \cos t \end{pmatrix}$$

in $SO(3)$ satisfies $\gamma'_{13}(0) = E_{13} - E_{31}$. This proves the theorem for $\mathbb{K} = \mathbb{R}$. We leave it to the reader in Exercise 5.1 to describe a natural basis of $u(n)$ and $sp(n)$ and construct a path tangent to each element of those bases. $\square$

Corollary 5.13.

(1) $\dim(SO(n)) = \frac{n(n-1)}{2}$.

(2) $\dim(U(n)) = n^2$.

(3) $\dim(Sp(n)) = 2n^2 + n$.

Proof. The n^2 entries of an n by n matrix include d below the diagonal, d above the diagonal, and n on the diagonal. So $n^2 = d + d + n$, which means $d = \frac{n^2 - n}{2}$. Skew-symmetric matrices have zeros on the diagonal, arbitrary real numbers above, and entries below determined by those above, so $\dim(so(n)) = d$. Skew-hermitian matrices have purely imaginary numbers on the diagonal and arbitrary complex numbers above the diagonal, so $\dim(u(n)) = 2d + n = n^2$. Skew-symplectic matrices have elements of the form $a\mathbf{i} + b\mathbf{j} + d\mathbf{k}$ along the diagonal and arbitrary quaternionic numbers above the diagonal, so $\dim(sp(n)) = 4d + 3n = 2n^2 + n$. $\square$

5. Exercises

Ex. 5.1. Complete the proof of Theorem 5.12.

Ex. 5.2. In the proof of Theorem 5.9, verify that $\alpha'(0) = A$.

Ex. 5.3. Prove that the product rule holds for non-square matrices.

Ex. 5.4. In Figure 2, how can you see visually that A and B both lie in $sl_2(\mathbb{R})$? Remember that a real 2×2 matrix with determinant 1 preserves the areas of parallelograms.

Ex. 5.5. Describe the Lie algebra of the affine group (see Exercise 3.11).

Ex. 5.6. Describe the Lie algebra of $\mathrm{Isom}(\mathbb{R}^n)$.

Ex. 5.7. Describe the Lie algebra of $UT_n(\mathbb{K})$ (see Exercise 4.12).

Ex. 5.8. Prove the Lie algebra of $\rho_n(GL_n(\mathbb{C})) \subset GL_{2n}(\mathbb{R})$ is equal to $\rho_n(gl_n(\mathbb{C}))$.

Ex. 5.9. Prove the Lie algebra of $\Psi_n(GL_n(\mathbb{H})) \subset GL_{2n}(\mathbb{C})$ is $\Psi_n(gl_n(\mathbb{H}))$.

Ex. 5.10. Prove that the tangent space to a matrix group G at $A \in G$ is:

$$T_A(G) = \{BA \mid B \in \mathfrak{g}(G)\} = \{AB \mid B \in \mathfrak{g}(G)\}.$$

Ex. 5.11. Give a geometric proof of the fact at the end of Section 3.

Ex. 5.12. Give an example of a 2-dimensional matrix group.

Ex. 5.13. Is Lemma 5.10 true for $\mathbb{K} = \mathbb{H}$?

Ex. 5.14. Describe the Lie algebra of $SL_n(\mathbb{H})$.

Ex. 5.15. Is part 3 of Lemma 5.11 valid when $\mathbb{K} \in \{\mathbb{C}, \mathbb{H}\}$?

Ex. 5.16. Let $\gamma : (-\epsilon, \epsilon) \to GL_n(\mathbb{K})$ be a differentiable path. Prove that the inverse path $t \mapsto \gamma(t)^{-1}$ is differentiable.
Hint: For $\mathbb{K} \in \{\mathbb{R}, \mathbb{C}\}$, use Cramer's rule.

Chapter 6

Matrix exponentiation

To prove Theorem 5.12, which said $\mathfrak{g}(\mathcal{O}_n(\mathbb{K})) = o_n(\mathbb{K})$, we constructed a differentiable path through the identity in $\mathcal{O}_n(\mathbb{K})$ in the direction of any A in a basis of $o_n(\mathbb{K})$. Our paths were defined with sines and cosines and seemed natural because they corresponded to families of rotations in certain planes. On the other hand, the paths we constructed to prove Theorem 5.9 (verifying the Lie algebra of $SL_n(\mathbb{K})$) seemed less natural. In general, is there a "best" path in the direction of any $A \in gl_n(\mathbb{K})$, and is this best path guaranteed to be contained in any matrix group $G \subset GL_n(\mathbb{K})$ to which A is a tangent vector? In this chapter, we construct optimal paths, which are called *one-parameter groups* and are defined in terms of *matrix exponentiation*. We begin the chapter with preliminary facts about series, which are necessary to understand matrix exponentiation.

1. Series in $\mathbb{K}$

We say that a series

$$\sum a_l = a_0 + a_1 + a_2 + \cdots$$

of elements $a_l \in \mathbb{K}$ <u>converges</u> if the corresponding sequence of partial sums

$$\{a_0, a_0 + a_1, a_0 + a_1 + a_2, ...\}$$

converges to some $a \in \mathbb{K}$. Here we are regarding $\mathbb{K}$ as $\mathbb{R}$, $\mathbb{R}^2$ or $\mathbb{R}^4$, and "convergence" means in the sense of Definition 4.6. In this case, we write $\sum a_l = a$. The series $\sum a_l$ is said to <u>converge absolutely</u> if $\sum |a_l|$ converges.

Proposition 6.1. *If $\sum a_l$ converges absolutely, then it converges.*

Proof. By the triangle inequality,

$$\left| \sum_{l=l_1}^{l_2} a_l \right| \leq \sum_{l=l_1}^{l_2} |a_l|.$$

The right side of this inequality is the distance between the l_2-th and the l_1-th partial sums of $\sum |a_l|$. The left side equals the distance between the l_2-th and the l_1-th partial sums of $\sum a_l$. If $\sum |a_l|$ converges, then its sequence of partial sums is Cauchy, so the inequality implies that the sequence of partial sums of $\sum a_l$ is also Cauchy and therefore convergent by Proposition 4.9.   □

One expects that the product of two series can be calculated by "infinitely distributing" and organizing terms by the sum of the indices, as in:

$$(a_0 + a_1 + a_2 + \cdots)(b_0 + b_1 + b_2 + \cdots)$$
$$= (a_0 b_0) + (a_0 b_1 + a_1 b_0) + (a_0 b_2 + a_1 b_1 + a_2 b_0) + \cdots.$$

This manipulation is justified by the following fact, which is proven in most analysis textbooks:

Proposition 6.2. *Suppose that $\sum a_l$ and $\sum b_l$ both converge, at least one absolutely. Let $c_l := \sum_{k=0}^{l} a_k b_{l-k}$. Then $\sum c_l = (\sum a_l)(\sum b_l)$.*

A <u>power series</u> means a "formal infinite-degree polynomial", that is, an expression of the form:

$$f(x) = c_0 + c_1 x + c_2 x^2 + c_3 x^3 + \cdots$$

with coefficients $c_i \in \mathbb{K}$. When the variable x is assigned a value in $\mathbb{K}$, the result is a series which may or may not converge. The <u>domain</u> of f means the set of all $x \in \mathbb{K}$ for which the series $f(x)$ converges. The next proposition says that the domain of any power series is a ball about the origin (possibly including some of its boundary and possibly with a radius of zero or infinity).

Proposition 6.3. *For any power series there exists an $R \in [0, \infty]$ (called its __radius of convergence__) such that $f(x)$ converges absolutely if $|x| < R$ and diverges if $|x| > R$.*

When $R = 0$, the series converges only at $x = 0$. When $R = \infty$, the series converges for all $x \in \mathbb{K}$.

Proof. The <u>root test</u> says that a series $\sum a_n$ converges absolutely if

$$\alpha := \limsup_{n \to \infty}(|a_n|)^{1/n}$$

is less than one, and diverges if α is greater than one. Even when $\mathbb{K} \in \{\mathbb{C}, \mathbb{H}\}$, this is essentially a statement about series of positive real numbers, so the $\mathbb{K} = \mathbb{R}$ proof found in any calculus textbook needs no alteration. In the series obtained by substituting $x \in \mathbb{K}$ into the power series $f(x) = \sum c_n x^n$,

$$\alpha = |x| \limsup_{n \to \infty}(|c_n|)^{1/n},$$

so the proposition holds with

$$R := \left(\limsup_{n \to \infty}(|c_n|)^{1/n} \right)^{-1}.$$

The interpretations of the extreme cases are: if $\limsup_{n \to \infty}(|c_n|)^{1/n}$ equals zero, then $R = \infty$, and if it equals ∞, then R equals zero. $\square$

In future applications, we will often restrict a power series to the real numbers in its domain. Such a restriction can be differentiated term-by-term as follows:

Proposition 6.4. *Let $f(x) = c_0 + c_1 x + c_2 x^2 + \cdots$ be a power series with radius of convergence R. The restriction of f to the real numbers in its domain, $f : (-R, R) \to \mathbb{K}$, is a differentiable path in $\mathbb{K}$ with derivative $f'(x) = c_1 + 2c_2 x + 3c_3 x^2 + \cdots$.*

Proof. The case $\mathbb{K} = \mathbb{R}$ is familiar from calculus, and the general case follows immediately from the real case. $\square$

2. Series in $M_n(\mathbb{K})$

We will also study series of matrices. We say that a series
$$\sum A_l = A_0 + A_1 + A_2 + \cdots$$
of elements $A_l \in M_n(\mathbb{K})$ converges (absolutely) if for each i, j the
series $(A_0)_{ij} + (A_1)_{ij} + (A_2)_{ij} + \cdots$ converges (absolutely) to some
$A_{ij} \in \mathbb{K}$. In this case, we write $\sum A_l = A$.

Proposition 6.2 generalizes to series of matrices.

Proposition 6.5. *Suppose that $\sum A_l$ and $\sum B_l$ both converge, at
least one absolutely. Let $C_l := \sum_{k=0}^{l} A_k B_{l-k}$. Then,*
$$\sum C_l = (\sum A_l)(\sum B_l).$$

The proof of Proposition 6.5 is left for Exercise 6.1. The idea is
to use Proposition 6.2 to prove that for all i, j,
$$\left(\sum C_l\right)_{ij} = \left(\left(\sum A_l\right)\left(\sum B_l\right)\right)_{ij}.$$

A power series $f(x) = c_0 + c_1 x + c_2 x^2 + \cdots$ with coefficients $c_i \in \mathbb{K}$
can be evaluated on a matrix $A \in M_n(\mathbb{K})$. The result is a series in
$M_n(\mathbb{K})$:
$$f(A) = c_0 I + c_1 A + c_2 A^2 + \cdots.$$

Proposition 6.6. *Let $f(x) = c_0 + c_1 x + c_2 x^2 + \cdots$ be a power series
with coefficients $c_i \in \mathbb{K}$ with radius of convergence R. If $A \in M_n(\mathbb{K})$
satisfies $|A| < R$, then $f(A) = c_0 I + c_1 A + c_2 A^2 + \cdots$ converges
absolutely.*

Remember that $|A|$ denotes the Euclidean norm on $M_n(\mathbb{K})$ re-
garded as $\mathbb{R}^{n^2}$, $\mathbb{R}^{2n^2}$ or $\mathbb{R}^{4n^2}$. For example,
$$\left|\begin{pmatrix} a + b\mathbf{i} & c + d\mathbf{i} \\ e + f\mathbf{i} & g + h\mathbf{i} \end{pmatrix}\right| = \sqrt{a^2 + b^2 + c^2 + d^2 + e^2 + f^2 + g^2 + h^2}.$$

Several other texts use an alternative norm on $M_n(\mathbb{K})$, defined as
$$||A|| := \sup\{|XA| \mid X \in \mathbb{K}^n \text{ with } |X| = 1\}.$$

Using this norm has the advantage that Proposition 6.6 becomes
sharper: if $||A|| < R$, then $f(A)$ converges absolutely, and if $||A|| > R$,
then $f(A)$ diverges. We will not use this "sup norm" in our text.

The proof of Proposition 6.6 will require an important lemma:

Lemma 6.7. *For all $X, Y \in M_n(\mathbb{K})$, $|XY| \leq |X| \cdot |Y|$.*

Proof. The proof depends on Proposition 3.7, the Schwarz inequality. For all indices i, j,

$$|(XY)_{ij}|^2 = \left| \sum_{l=1}^{n} X_{il} Y_{lj} \right|^2 = \left| \langle (\text{row } i \text{ of } X), (\text{column } j \text{ of } \overline{Y})^T \rangle \right|^2$$

$$\leq |(\text{row } i \text{ of } X)|^2 \cdot \left| (\text{column } j \text{ of } \overline{Y})^T \right|^2$$

$$= \left(\sum_{l=1}^{n} |X_{il}|^2 \right) \cdot \left(\sum_{l=1}^{n} |Y_{lj}|^2 \right).$$

Summing over all indices i, j gives:

$$|XY|^2 = \sum_{i,j=1}^{n} |(XY)_{ij}|^2 \leq \sum_{i,j=1}^{n} \left(\left(\sum_{l=1}^{n} |X_{il}|^2 \right) \cdot \left(\sum_{l=1}^{n} |Y_{lj}|^2 \right) \right)$$

$$= \left(\sum_{i,j=1}^{n} |X_{ij}|^2 \right) \cdot \left(\sum_{i,j=1}^{n} |Y_{ij}|^2 \right) = |X|^2 |Y|^2.$$

$\square$

Proof of Proposition 6.6. For any indices i, j, we must prove that

$$|(c_o I)_{ij}| + |(c_1 A)_{ij}| + |(c_2 A^2)_{ij}| + \cdots$$

converges. The lth term of this series satisfies:

$$|(c_l A^l)_{ij}| \leq |c_l A^l| = |c_l| \cdot |A^l| \leq |c_l| \cdot |A|^l.$$

Since $|A|$ is less than the radius of convergence of f, the result follows.

$\square$

When the power series of the function $f(x) = e^x$ is applied to a matrix $A \in M_n(\mathbb{K})$, the result is called <u>matrix exponentiation</u>:

$$e^A = I + A + (1/2!)A^2 + (1/3!)A^3 + (1/4!)A^4 + \cdots .$$

The radius of convergence of this power series is ∞, so by Proposition 6.6, e^A converges absolutely for all $A \in M_n(\mathbb{K})$. As you might guess from its appearance as the chapter title, matrix exponentiation is a central idea in the study of matrix groups.

3. The best path in a matrix group

In this section, we use matrix exponentiation to construct canonical "best paths" in each given direction of a matrix group. Let's begin with a simple example. Figure 1 illustrates the vector field associated to

$$A := \begin{pmatrix} 0 & 1 \\ -1 & 0 \end{pmatrix} \in so(2).$$

What is the most natural differentiable path $\gamma(t)$ in $SO(2)$ with $\gamma(0) = I$ and $\gamma'(0) = A$? The choice $\gamma(t) := I + tA$ seems natural, but is not in $SO(2)$. Every path in $SO(2)$ through A has the form:

$$\gamma(t) := \begin{pmatrix} \cos f(t) & \sin f(t) \\ -\sin f(t) & \cos f(t) \end{pmatrix},$$

where $f(t)$ is a differentiable function with $f(0) = 0$ and $f'(0) = 1$. The choice $f(t) = t$ is clearly the most natural choice; what visual property does this path $\gamma(t)$ have that no other candidate shares? The answer is that for every $X \in \mathbb{R}^2$, the path $\alpha(t) := R_{\gamma(t)}(X)$ is an *integral curve* of the vector field R_A. This means that the vector field R_A tells the direction that X is moved by the family of linear transformations associated to $\gamma(t)$ for all time rather than just initially at $t = 0$; more precisely,

Definition 6.8. *A path $\alpha : (-\epsilon, \epsilon) \to \mathbb{R}^m$ is called an integral curve of a vector field $F : \mathbb{R}^m \to \mathbb{R}^m$ if $\alpha'(t) = F(\alpha(t))$ for all $t \in (-\epsilon, \epsilon)$.*

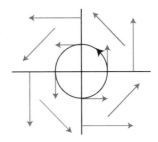

Figure 1. An integral curve of R_A.

For the matrix A above, the integral curves of R_A are (segments of) circles centered at the origin, parameterized counterclockwise with speed one radian per unit time.

More generally, if $A \in gl_n(\mathbb{K})$, we would like to find the "most natural" path $\gamma(t)$ in $GL_n(\mathbb{K})$ with $\gamma(0) = I$ and $\gamma'(0) = A$. We will attempt to choose $\gamma(t)$ such that for all $X \in \mathbb{K}^n$, the path

$$t \mapsto R_{\gamma(t)}(X)$$

is an integral curve of R_A. You might find it surprising that a single path $\gamma(t)$ will work for all choices of X.

The trick is to find a power series expression for the integral curve $\alpha(t)$ of R_A beginning at $\alpha(0) = X$. We contrive coefficients $c_i \in \mathbb{K}^n$ such that the path $\alpha : \mathbb{R} \to \mathbb{K}^n$ defined by the power series

$$\alpha(t) = c_0 + c_1 t + c_2 t^2 + c_3 t^3 + \cdots$$

is an integral curve of R_A with $\alpha(0) = c_0 = X$. Being an integral curve means that $\alpha'(t)$ (which is $c_1 + 2c_2 t + 3c_3 t^2 + \cdots$) equals $R_A(\alpha(t))$ (which is $c_0 A + c_1 t A + c_2 t^2 A + c_3 t^3 A + \cdots$). So we want:

$$(c_1 + 2c_2 t + 3c_3 t^2 + \cdots) = (c_0 A + c_1 t A + c_2 t^2 A + c_3 t^3 A + \cdots).$$

Equating coefficients of corresponding powers of t gives the recursive formula $lc_l = c_{l-1} A$. Together with the initial condition $c_0 = X$, this gives the explicit formula $c_l = \frac{1}{l!} X A^l$, so the integral curve is:

$$\begin{aligned} \alpha(t) &= X + XtA + \frac{X}{2!}(tA)^2 + \frac{X}{3!}(tA)^3 + \cdots \\ &= Xe^{tA} = R_{e^{tA}}(X). \end{aligned}$$

In summary, the path $\gamma(t) = e^{tA}$ has the desired property that for all $X \in \mathbb{K}^n$, $\alpha(t) = R_{\gamma(t)}(X)$ is an integral curve of R_A. This could also have been proven quickly from scratch using:

Proposition 6.9. *Let $A \in gl_n(\mathbb{K})$. The path $\gamma : \mathbb{R} \to M_n(\mathbb{K})$ defined as $\gamma(t) := e^{tA}$ is differentiable, and $\gamma'(t) = A \cdot \gamma(t) = \gamma(t) \cdot A$.*

Proof. Each of the n^2 entries of

$$\gamma(t) = e^{tA} = I + tA + (1/2)t^2A^2 + (1/6)t^3A^3 + \cdots$$

is a power series in t, which by Proposition 6.4 can be termwise differentiated, giving:

$$\gamma'(t) = 0 + A + tA^2 + (1/2)t^2A^3 + \cdots.$$

This equals $\gamma(t) \cdot A$ or $A \cdot \gamma(t)$ depending on whether you factor an A out on the left or right. $\qquad\square$

There are two interesting interpretations of Proposition 6.9, the first which we've already discussed:

Proposition 6.10. *Let $A \in M_n(\mathbb{K})$ and let $\gamma(t) = e^{tA}$.*

(1) *For all $X \in \mathbb{K}^n$, $\alpha(t) = R_{\gamma(t)}(X)$ is an integral curve of R_A. Also, $\alpha(t) = L_{\gamma(t)}(X)$ is an integral curve of L_A.*

(2) *$\gamma(t)$ is itself an integral curve of the vector field on $M_n(\mathbb{K})$ whose value at g is $A \cdot g$ (and is also an integral curve of the vector field whose value at g is $g \cdot A$).*

Both (1) and (2) follow immediately from Proposition 6.4. The two parts have different pictures and different uses. It is interesting that the left and right versions of part (2) can simultaneously be true, since the two vector fields on $M_n(\mathbb{K})$ do not agree. Evidently, they must agree along the image of γ.

4. Properties of the exponential map

The exponential map $\exp : M_n(\mathbb{K}) \to M_n(\mathbb{K})$, which sends $A \mapsto e^A$ is a powerful tool for studying matrix groups. We have already seen that exp restricted to a real line is a "best path". In this section, we derive important algebraic properties of the exponential map, which further justify our use of the term "exponential".

Proposition 6.11. *If $AB = BA$, then $e^{A+B} = e^A \cdot e^B$.*

Proof. By Proposition 6.5,

$$\begin{aligned}
e^A e^B &= (I + A + (1/2)A^2 + \cdots)(I + B + (1/2)B^2 + \cdots) \\
&= I + (A + B) + ((1/2)A^2 + AB + (1/2)B^2) + \cdots.
\end{aligned}$$

On the other hand,

$$
\begin{aligned}
e^{A+B} &= I + (A+B) + (1/2)(A+B)^2 + \cdots \\
&= I + (A+B) + (1/2)(A^2 + AB + BA + B^2) + \cdots .
\end{aligned}
$$

Since $AB = BA$, the first terms of $e^A e^B$ equal the first terms of e^{A+B}. To verify that the pattern continues:

$$
\begin{aligned}
e^A e^B &= \left(\sum_{l=0}^{\infty} \frac{A^l}{l!} \right) \left(\sum_{l=0}^{\infty} \frac{B^l}{l!} \right) = \sum_{l=0}^{\infty} \sum_{k=0}^{l} \frac{A^k B^{l-k}}{k!(l-k)!} \\
&= \sum_{l=0}^{\infty} \frac{1}{l!} \sum_{k=0}^{l} \binom{l}{k} A^k B^{l-k} = \sum_{l=0}^{\infty} \frac{(A+B)^l}{l!} .
\end{aligned}
$$

The last equality uses the fact that A and B commute. $\square$

Since most pairs of matrices do not commute, you might not expect Proposition 6.11 to have much use, except in the $n = 1$ case. Surprisingly, the proposition has many strong consequences, including every proposition in the remainder of this section.

Proposition 6.12. *For any $A \in M_n(\mathbb{K})$, $e^A \in GL_n(\mathbb{K})$. Therefore, matrix exponentiation is a map $\exp : gl_n(\mathbb{K}) \to GL_n(\mathbb{K})$.*

Proof. Since A and $-A$ commute, $e^A \cdot e^{-A} = e^{A-A} = e^0 = I$, so e^A has inverse e^{-A}. $\square$

We will see later that the image of $\exp$ contains a neighborhood of I in $M_n(\mathbb{K})$, so it may seem counterintuitive that this image misses all of the singular matrices.

Proposition 6.13. *If $A \in o_n(\mathbb{K})$, then $e^A \in \mathcal{O}_n(\mathbb{K})$.*

Proof. Since $A \in o_n(\mathbb{K})$, $A^* = -A$. Therefore,

$$
e^A \left(e^A \right)^* = e^A e^{A^*} = e^A e^{-A} = e^{A-A} = e^0 = I.
$$

So $e^A \in \mathcal{O}_n(\mathbb{K})$ by part (4) of Proposition 3.9. Exercise 6.2 asks you to verify that $(e^A)^* = e^{A^*}$, which was used in the first equality above. $\square$

This proposition allows a cleaner proof of Theorem 5.12, which says that $o_n(\mathbb{K})$ is the Lie algebra of $\mathcal{O}_n(\mathbb{K})$. How? If $A \in o_n(\mathbb{K})$, then $\gamma(t) = e^{tA}$ is a differentiable path in $\mathcal{O}_n(\mathbb{K})$ with $\gamma'(0) = A$. This proves that $o_n(\mathbb{K}) \subset \mathfrak{g}(\mathcal{O}_n(\mathbb{K}))$, which was the more difficult inclusion to verify.

Since $SU(n) = U(n) \cap SL_n(\mathbb{C})$, one expects the Lie algebra $su(n)$ of $SU(n)$ to equal the set of trace-zero skew-hermitian matrices:

Proposition 6.14. $su(n) = u(n) \cap sl_n(\mathbb{C})$.

The inclusion $su(n) \subset u(n) \cap sl_n(\mathbb{C})$ is trivial. For the other inclusion, we must construct a path in $SU(n)$ tangent to any $A \in u(n) \cap sl_n(\mathbb{C})$. The path $\gamma(t) = e^{tA}$ is contained in $U(n)$, but we have yet to verify that it is contained in $SL_n(\mathbb{C})$, which follows from:

Lemma 6.15. *Let* $\mathbb{K} \in \{\mathbb{R}, \mathbb{C}\}$. *For any* $A \in M_n(\mathbb{K})$,
$$\det(e^A) = e^{trace(A)}.$$

Proof. Let $f(t) = \det(e^{tA})$. Its derivative is:
$$
\begin{aligned}
f'(t) &= \lim_{h \to 0} (1/h)(\det(e^{(t+h)A}) - \det(e^{tA})) \\
&= \lim_{h \to 0} (1/h)(\det(e^{tA}e^{hA}) - \det(e^{tA})) \\
&= \lim_{h \to 0} (1/h)(\det(e^{tA}))(\det(e^{hA}) - 1) \\
&= (\det(e^{tA})) \lim_{h \to 0} (1/h)(\det(e^{hA}) - 1) \\
&= f(t) \frac{d}{dt}\Big|_{t=0} e^{tA} \\
&= f(t) \cdot \text{trace}(A).
\end{aligned}
$$

The last equality follows from Lemma 5.10. Since $f(0) = 1$ and
$$f'(t) = f(t) \cdot \text{trace}(A),$$
the unique solution for f is $f(t) = e^{t \cdot \text{trace}(A)}$. In particular,
$$f(1) = \det(e^A) = e^{\text{trace}(A)}.$$

$\square$

For $A \in gl_n(\mathbb{K})$, we have verified that the path $\gamma(t) := e^{tA}$ has several geometric and analytic properties. It also has an important algebraic property; namely, its image is a subgroup of $GL_n(\mathbb{K})$. To elaborate this comment, we make the following definition, in which $(\mathbb{R}, +)$ denotes the group of real numbers under the operation of addition.

Definition 6.16. *A one parameter group in a matrix group G is a differentiable group-homomorphism $\gamma : (\mathbb{R}, +) \to G$.*

"Homomorphism" means that $\gamma(t_1 + t_2) = \gamma(t_1)\gamma(t_2)$. A one-parameter group is both an algebraic object (a homomorphism) and a geometric object (a differentiable path). The interplay between algebra and geometry is what makes matrix groups so rich in structure.

Proposition 6.17.

(1) *For every $A \in gl_n(\mathbb{K})$, $\gamma(t) := e^{tA}$ is a one parameter group.*

(2) *Every one parameter group in $GL_n(\mathbb{K})$ has the description $\gamma(t) = e^{tA}$ for some $A \in gl_n(\mathbb{K})$.*

Proof. Part (1) follows from Proposition 6.11, since:

$$\gamma(t_1 + t_2) = e^{t_1 A + t_2 A} = e^{t_1 A} e^{t_2 A} = \gamma(t_1)\gamma(t_2).$$

Notice in particular that $\gamma(t) \cdot \gamma(-t) = I$, which shows that

$$\gamma(t)^{-1} = \gamma(-t).$$

For part (2), suppose $\gamma(t)$ is a one-parameter group in $GL_n(\mathbb{K})$. Let $A := \gamma'(0)$. Notice that for all $t \in \mathbb{R}$,

$$\gamma'(t) = \lim_{h \to 0} \frac{1}{h}(\gamma(t+h) - \gamma(t)) = \gamma(t) \lim_{h \to 0} \frac{1}{h}(\gamma(h) - I) = \gamma(t)A.$$

Since $\gamma'(t) = \gamma(t)A$, we suspect (by comparing to Proposition 6.9) that $\gamma(t) = e^{tA}$. This is verified by applying the product rule:

$$\begin{aligned} \frac{d}{dt}(\gamma(t)e^{-tA}) &= \gamma'(t)e^{-tA} + \gamma(t)\frac{d}{dt}(e^{-tA}) \\ &= \gamma(t)Ae^{-tA} - \gamma(t)Ae^{-tA} = 0. \end{aligned}$$

So $\gamma(t)e^{-tA} = I$, which implies that $\gamma(t) = e^{tA}$. $\qquad\square$

Finally, we describe how conjugation and exponentiation relate:

Proposition 6.18. *For all* $A, B \in M_n(\mathbb{K})$ *with* A *invertible,*

$$e^{ABA^{-1}} = Ae^B A^{-1}.$$

Proof.

$$
\begin{aligned}
Ae^B A^{-1} &= A(I + B + (1/2)B^2 + (1/6)B^3 + \cdots)A^{-1} \\
&= I + ABA^{-1} + (1/2)AB^2 A^{-1} + (1/6)AB^3 A^{-1} + \cdots \\
&= I + ABA^{-1} + (1/2)(ABA^{-1})^2 + (1/6)(ABA^{-1})^3 + \cdots \\
&= e^{ABA^{-1}}.
\end{aligned}
$$

$\square$

5. Exercises

Ex. 6.1. Prove Proposition 6.5.

Ex. 6.2. Prove that $(e^A)^* = e^{A^*}$ for all $A \in M_n(\mathbb{K})$.

Ex. 6.3.

(1) Let $A = \text{diag}(a_1, a_2, ..., a_n) \in M_n(\mathbb{R})$. Calculate e^A. Using this, give a simple proof that $\det(e^A) = e^{\text{trace}(A)}$ when A is diagonal.

(2) Give a simple proof that $\det(e^A) = e^{\text{trace}(A)}$ when A is conjugate to a diagonal matrix.

Ex. 6.4. Let $A = \begin{pmatrix} 0 & 1 \\ -1 & 0 \end{pmatrix}$. Calculate e^A.

Ex. 6.5. Can a one parameter group ever cross itself?

Ex. 6.6. Describe all one parameter groups in $GL_1(\mathbb{C})$. Draw several in the xy-plane.

Ex. 6.7. Let $G = \left\{ \begin{pmatrix} x & y \\ 0 & 1 \end{pmatrix} \in GL_2(\mathbb{R}) \middle| x > 0 \right\}$. Describe the one parameter groups in G, and draw several in the xy-plane.

Ex. 6.8. Visually describe the path $\gamma(t) = e^{t\mathbf{j}}$ in $Sp(1) \cong S^3$.

Ex. 6.9. Let $A = \begin{pmatrix} a & b \\ -b & a \end{pmatrix} \in gl_2(\mathbb{R})$. Calculate e^A (*Hint: Write A as the sum of two commuting matrices*). Draw the vector field R_A when $a = 1$ and $b = 2$, and sketch some integral curves.

Ex. 6.10. Repeat the previous problem with $A = \begin{pmatrix} a & b \\ b & a \end{pmatrix}$.

Ex. 6.11. When A is in the Lie algebra of $UT_n(\mathbb{K})$, prove that $e^A \in UT_n(\mathbb{K})$ (see Exercise 4.12).

Ex. 6.12. When A is in the Lie algebra of $\mathrm{Isom}(\mathbb{R}^n)$, prove that $e^A \in \mathrm{Isom}(\mathbb{R}^n)$.

Ex. 6.13. Describe the one-parameter groups is $\mathrm{Trans}(\mathbb{R}^n)$.

Ex. 6.14. The multiplicative group of positive real numbers can be identified with the subgroup: $G = \{(a) \in GL_1(\mathbb{R}) \mid a > 0\}$. Given A in the Lie algebra of G, describe the vector field on G associated to A, as part (2) of Proposition 6.10. Solve for the integral curve of this vector field beginning at (1).

Chapter 7

Matrix groups are manifolds

In this chapter we prove two crucial facts about how the exponential map restricts to a Lie algebra. For $r > 0$, denote

$$B_r := \{W \in M_n(\mathbb{K}) \mid |W| < r\}.$$

Theorem 7.1. *Let $G \subset GL_n(\mathbb{K})$ be a matrix group, with Lie algebra $\mathfrak{g} \subset gl_n(\mathbb{K})$.*

    (1) *For all $X \in \mathfrak{g}$, $e^X \in G$.*

    (2) *For sufficiently small $r > 0$, $V := \exp(B_r \cap \mathfrak{g})$ is a neighborhood of I in G, and the restriction $\exp : B_r \cap \mathfrak{g} \to V$ is a homeomorphism.*

Part (1) says that if a one parameter group in $GL_n(\mathbb{K})$ begins tangent to a matrix group G, then it lies entirely in G. In the previous chapter, we verified (1) when $G \in \{GL_n(\mathbb{K}), \mathcal{O}_n(\mathbb{K}), SL_n(\mathbb{R}), SL_n(\mathbb{C}), SU(n)\}$. However, the proofs were different in each case, and new ideas are needed in this chapter to generalize to arbitrary matrix groups.

Part (2) has not yet been verified for any familiar matrix groups. We will actually prove the stronger statement that $\exp : B_r \cap \mathfrak{g} \to V$ is a *diffeomorphism* (which will be defined in this chapter, but roughly means differentiable homeomorphism).

A beautiful corollary of Theorem 7.1 is that every matrix group is a manifold, which we will carefully define in this chapter. Roughly, a manifold is a nice subset of Euclidean space; at every point p its tangent space is a subspace, and a neighborhood of p is diffeomorphic to a neighborhood of 0 in the tangent space. Manifolds are central to modern mathematics. Their investigation is the starting point of several branches of geometry.

1. Analysis background

In this section, we review some concepts from analysis which are necessary to prove Theorem 7.1, including the inverse function theorem.

Let $U \subset \mathbb{R}^m$ be an open set. Any function $f : U \to \mathbb{R}^n$ can be thought of as n separate functions; we write $f = (f_1, ..., f_n)$, where each $f_i : U \to \mathbb{R}$. For example, the function $f : \mathbb{R}^2 \to \mathbb{R}^3$ defined as

$$f(x, y) = (\sin(x + y), e^{xy}, x^2 - y^3)$$

splits as $f_1(x, y) = \sin(x + y)$, $f_2(x, y) = e^{xy}$ and $f_3(x, y) = x^2 - y^3$.

Let $p \in U$ and let $v \in \mathbb{R}^m$. The <u>directional derivative</u> of f in the direction v at p is defined as:

$$df_p(v) := \lim_{t \to 0} \frac{f(p + tv) - f(p)}{t},$$

if this limit exists.

The directional derivative can be interpreted visually by considering the straight line $\gamma(t) = p + tv$ in $\mathbb{R}^m$. If the initial velocity vector of the image path $(f \circ \gamma)(t) = f(p + tv)$ in $\mathbb{R}^n$ exists, it is called $df_p(v)$. In other words, $df_p(v)$ approximates where f sends points near p in the direction of v; see Figure 1.

The directional derivatives of the component functions $\{f_1, ..., f_n\}$ in the directions of the standard orthonormal basis vectors $\{e_1, ..., e_m\}$ of $\mathbb{R}^m$ are called <u>partial derivatives</u> of f and are denoted as:

$$\frac{\partial f_i}{\partial x_j}(p) := d(f_i)_p(e_j).$$

They measure the rates at which the component functions change in the coordinate directions. For fixed $\{i, j\}$, if $\frac{\partial f_i}{\partial x_j}(p)$ exists at each

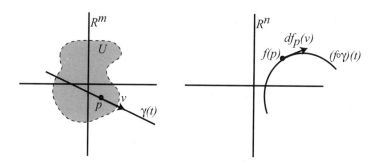

Figure 1. $df_p(v)$ is the initial velocity vector of the image under f of the straight line $\gamma(t)$ in the direction of v.

$p \in U$, then $p \mapsto \frac{\partial f_i}{\partial x_j}(p)$ is another function from U to $\mathbb{R}$; its partial derivatives (if they exist) are called second order partial derivatives of f, and so on.

The function f is called C^r _on_ U if all r^{th} order partial derivatives exist and are continuous on U, and f is called smooth on U if f is C^r on U for all positive integers r. The following is proven in any real analysis textbook:

Proposition 7.2. _If_ f _is_ C^1 _on_ U, _then for all_ $p \in U$,

(1) $v \mapsto df_p(v)$ _is a linear function from_ $\mathbb{R}^m$ _to_ $\mathbb{R}^n$.

(2) $f(q) \approx f(p) + df_p(q - p)$ _is a good approximation of_ f _near_ p _in the following sense: for any infinite sequence_ $\{q_1, q_2, ...\}$ _of points in_ $\mathbb{R}^m$ _converging to_ p,

$$\lim_{t \to \infty} \frac{f(q_t) - f(p) - df_p(q_t - p)}{|q_t - p|} = 0.$$

Proposition 7.2 says that if f is C^1 on U, then the directional derivatives of f are well-behaved at any $p \in U$. It is useful to turn this conclusion into a definition.

Definition 7.3. $f : \mathbb{R}^m \to \mathbb{R}^n$ _is called_ differentiable _at_ $p \in \mathbb{R}^m$ _if_ $df_p(v)$ _exists for every_ $v \in \mathbb{R}^m$, _and properties (1) and (2) of Proposition 7.2 hold. In this case, the linear function_ df_p _is called the_ derivative of f at p.

Notice that it is not enough for all directional derivatives to exist at p; we require the function $v \mapsto df_p(v)$ to be linear and to approximate f well near p before we are willing to call f differentiable at p or to refer to the function df_p as its derivative.

If f is C^1 on a neighborhood of p, then $df_p = L_A = R_{A^T}$, where $A \in M_{n,m}(\mathbb{R})$ is the matrix of all first order partial derivatives of f:

$$A = \begin{pmatrix} \frac{\partial f_1}{\partial x_1}(p) & \cdots & \frac{\partial f_1}{\partial x_m}(p) \\ \vdots & \ddots & \vdots \\ \frac{\partial f_n}{\partial x_1}(p) & \cdots & \frac{\partial f_n}{\partial x_m}(p) \end{pmatrix}.$$

When $n = 1$, this is familiar from multivariable calculus: directional derivatives are computed by dotting with the gradient. The $n > 1$ case follows by applying this fact to each component function f_i.

The derivative of a composition of two functions turns out to be the composition of their derivatives:

Proposition 7.4 (Chain rule). *Suppose $\gamma : \mathbb{R}^l \to \mathbb{R}^m$ is differentiable at $x \in \mathbb{R}^l$ and $f : \mathbb{R}^m \to \mathbb{R}^n$ is differentiable at $\gamma(x)$. Then their composition is differentiable at x, and*

$$d(f \circ \gamma)_x = df_{\gamma(x)} \circ d\gamma_x.$$

The chain rule is an important tool, and some comments about it are in order. First, γ need not be defined on all of $\mathbb{R}^l$, but only on a neighborhood of x for the chain rule to be valid. Similarly, it is enough that f be defined on a neighborhood of $\gamma(x)$.

Second, the case $l = 1$ has an important visual interpretation. In this case, γ is a path in $\mathbb{R}^m$ and $f \circ \gamma$ is the image path in $\mathbb{R}^n$. Set $x = 0$ and $p = \gamma(0)$. The chain rule says that for all $v \in \mathbb{R}$,

$$d(f \circ \gamma)_0(v) = df_p(d\gamma_0(v)).$$

Choosing v as the unit-vector $v = e_1 \in \mathbb{R}^1$ gives:

$$(f \circ \gamma)'(0) = df_p(\gamma'(0)).$$

This provides an important interpretation of the derivative of a function $f : \mathbb{R}^m \to \mathbb{R}^n$ at $p \in \mathbb{R}^m$:

Proposition 7.5. $df_p(v)$ *is the initial velocity vector of the image under f of any differentiable path $\gamma(t)$ in $\mathbb{R}^m$ with $\gamma(0) = p$ and $\gamma'(0) = v$.*

This proposition says Figure 1 remains valid when the straight line $\gamma(t)$ is replaced by any (possibly curved) path $\gamma(t)$ with $\gamma(0) = p$ and $\gamma'(0) = v$. This proposition is so useful, we will take it as our definition of $df_p(v)$ in the remainder of the book.

Another important consequence of the chain rule is that the derivative of an invertible function is an element of the general linear group. More precisely, suppose that $U \subset \mathbb{R}^n$ is open and $f : U \to \mathbb{R}^n$ is an invertible function from U to its image $f(U)$. Suppose that f is differentiable at $x \in U$ and f^{-1} is differentiable at $f(x)$. The chain rule says:

$$d(f^{-1} \circ f)_x = d(f^{-1})_{f(x)} \circ df_x.$$

On the other hand, $f^{-1} \circ f$ is the identify function, whose derivative at any point is the identify map. So $d(f^{-1})_{f(x)} \circ df_x$ is the identity linear map, which means that df_x is an invertible linear map (the corresponding matrix is an element of $GL_n(\mathbb{R})$).

A crucial result from analysis is the following converse:

Theorem 7.6 (Inverse function theorem). *If $f : \mathbb{R}^n \to \mathbb{R}^n$ is C^r on a neighborhood of $x \in \mathbb{R}^n$ ($r \geq 1$) and df_x is an invertible linear map, then there exists a (possibly smaller) neighborhood U of x such that $V := f(U)$ is a neighborhood of $f(x)$, and $f : U \to V$ is invertible with C^r inverse.*

The inverse function theorem is quite remarkable. It reduces the seemingly difficult problem of deciding whether f is locally invertible near x to the computationally simple task of checking whether the determinant of the linear map df_x is non-zero! The proof is non-trivial, but the theorem is believable, since $f(y) \approx f(x) + df_x(y - x)$ is a first-order approximation of f near x. The theorem says that if this first-order approximation is bijective, then f is bijective near x.

2. Proof of part (1) of Theorem 7.1

Let $G \subset GL_n(\mathbb{K})$ be a matrix group with Lie algebra $\mathfrak{g}$. Part (1) of Theorem 7.1 says that for all $X \in \mathfrak{g}$, $e^X \in G$. We verified this for several groups. Another reason to expect the theorem to be true comes from the following idea. The tangent space to G at I is $\mathfrak{g}$, and the tangent space at $a \in G$ is

$$T_a G = a \cdot \mathfrak{g} := \{a \cdot Y \mid Y \in \mathfrak{g}\}$$

(by Exercise 5.10). Fix a vector $X \in \mathfrak{g}$. Consider the vector field $\mathcal{V}$ on $M_n(\mathbb{K})$ whose value at $a \in M_n(\mathbb{K})$ is $\mathcal{V}(a) := a \cdot X$. At points of G, this vector field is tangent to G. The path $\gamma(t) = e^{tX}$ is an integral curve of $\mathcal{V}$, because $\gamma'(t) = \gamma(t) \cdot X$ (see Proposition 6.10). Since $\gamma(0) = I \in G$, we expect $\gamma(t)$ to remain in G.

It would be nice to know that G is a manifold, since an integral curve of a smooth vector field on Euclidean space which at points of a manifold M is tangent to M must remain on M if it begins on M. But we're getting ahead of ourselves, since we haven't defined manifold, and we will need Theorem 7.1 in order to prove that matrix groups are manifolds. To avoid circular reasoning, we must abandon the argument, although the following proof (from [11]) does reflect some of its essence.

Proof of part (1) of Theorem 7.1. Let $\{X_1, ..., X_k\}$ be a basis of $\mathfrak{g}$. For each $i = 1, ..., k$ choose a differentiable path $\alpha_i : (-\epsilon, \epsilon) \to G$ with $\alpha_i(0) = I$ and $\alpha_i'(0) = X_i$. Define

$$F_{\mathfrak{g}} : (\text{neighborhood of } 0 \text{ in } \mathfrak{g}) \to G$$

as follows:

$$F_{\mathfrak{g}}(c_1 X_1 + \cdots + c_k X_k) = \alpha_1(c_1) \cdot \alpha_2(c_2) \cdots \alpha_k(c_k).$$

Notice that $F_{\mathfrak{g}}(0) = I$, and $d(F_{\mathfrak{g}})_0$ is the identify function:

$$d(F_{\mathfrak{g}})_0(X) = X \text{ for all } X \in \mathfrak{g},$$

as is easily verified on basis elements.

Choose a subspace $\mathfrak{p} \subset M_n(\mathbb{K})$ which is complementary to $\mathfrak{g}$, which means completing the set $\{X_1, ..., X_k\}$ to a basis of all of $M_n(\mathbb{K})$

and defining $\mathfrak{p}$ as the span of the added basis elements. So $M_n(\mathbb{K}) = \mathfrak{g} \times \mathfrak{p}$.

Choose a function $F_{\mathfrak{p}} : \mathfrak{p} \to M_n(\mathbb{K})$ with $F_{\mathfrak{p}}(0) = I$ and with $d(F_{\mathfrak{p}})_0(V) = V$ for all $V \in \mathfrak{p}$. For example, $F_{\mathfrak{p}}(V) := I + V$ works. Next define the function

$$F : (\text{neighborhood of } 0 \text{ in } \mathfrak{g} \times \mathfrak{p} = M_n(\mathbb{K})) \to M_n(\mathbb{K})$$

by the rule $F(X+Y) = F_{\mathfrak{g}}(X) \cdot F_{\mathfrak{p}}(Y)$ for all $X \in \mathfrak{g}$ and $Y \in \mathfrak{p}$. Notice that $F(0) = I$ and dF_0 is the identity function: $dF_0(X+Y) = X+Y$.

By the inverse function theorem, F has an inverse function defined on a neighborhood of I in $M_n(\mathbb{K})$. Express the inverse as follows for matrices a in this neighborhood:

$$F^{-1}(a) = u(a) + v(a) \in \mathfrak{g} \times \mathfrak{p}.$$

By definition, $u(F(X + Y)) = X$ and $v(F(X + Y)) = Y$ for all $X \in \mathfrak{g}$ and $Y \in \mathfrak{p}$ near 0. The important thing is that v tests whether an element $a \in M_n(\mathbb{K})$ near I lies in G:

$$v(a) = 0 \implies a \in G.$$

Let $X \in \mathfrak{g}$ and define $a(t) = e^{tX}$. We wish to prove that $a(t) \in G$ for small t by showing that $v(a(t)) = 0$. Since $v(a(0)) = 0$, it will suffice to prove that $\frac{d}{dt}v(a(t)) = 0$ for small t. Since

$$\frac{d}{dt}v(a(t)) = dv_{a(t)}(a'(t)) = dv_{a(t)}(X \cdot a(t)),$$

the result will follow from the following lemma:

Lemma 7.7. *For all $a \in M_n(\mathbb{K})$ near I and all $X \in \mathfrak{g}$, $dv_a(X \cdot a) = 0$.*

Proof. Express a as:

$$a = F(Z + Y) = F_{\mathfrak{g}}(Z) \cdot F_{\mathfrak{p}}(Y),$$

where $Z \in \mathfrak{g}$ and $Y \in \mathfrak{p}$. For all $W \in \mathfrak{g}$, and for sufficiently small t,

$$v(F_{\mathfrak{g}}(Z + tW) \cdot F_{\mathfrak{p}}(Y)) = Y,$$

which means that v is not changing at a in these directions:

$$
\begin{aligned}
0 &= \left.\frac{d}{dt}\right|_{t=0} v(F_{\mathfrak{g}}(Z+tW) \cdot F_{\mathfrak{p}}(Y)) \\
&= dv_a((d(F_{\mathfrak{g}})_Z(W)) \cdot F_{\mathfrak{p}}(Y)) \\
&= dv_a((d(F_{\mathfrak{g}})_Z(W)) \cdot F_{\mathfrak{g}}(Z)^{-1} \cdot a) \\
&= dv_a(X \cdot a),
\end{aligned}
$$

where $X := (d(F_{\mathfrak{g}})_Z(W)) \cdot F_{\mathfrak{g}}(Z)^{-1}$. It remains to prove that X is an arbitrary element of $\mathfrak{g}$. First, $X \in \mathfrak{g}$ because it is the initial tangent vector of the following path in G:

$$
t \mapsto F_{\mathfrak{g}}(Z+tW) \cdot F_{\mathfrak{g}}(Z)^{-1}.
$$

Second, X is arbitrary because the linear map from $\mathfrak{g} \to \mathfrak{g}$ which sends

$$
W \mapsto (d(F_{\mathfrak{g}})_Z(W)) \cdot F_{\mathfrak{g}}(Z)^{-1}
$$

is the identity map when $Z = 0$, and so by continuity has determinant close to 1, and is therefore an isomorphism, when Z is close to 0. In other words, W can be chosen so that X is any element of $\mathfrak{g}$. $\square$

The lemma completes our proof that if $X \in \mathfrak{g}$, then $e^{tX} \in G$ for small t, say for $t \in (-\epsilon, \epsilon)$. The result can be extended by observing that for all $t \in (-\epsilon, \epsilon)$ and all positive integers N,

$$
e^{NtX} = e^{tX + tX + \cdots + tX} = e^{tX} \cdot e^{tX} \cdots e^{tX} \in G.
$$

This verifies that $e^{tX} \in G$ for all $t \in \mathbb{R}$, which completes the proof!
$\square$

3. Proof of part (2) of Theorem 7.1

It can be shown that any power series gives a smooth function on the set of matrices with norm less than its radius of convergence. In particular:

Proposition 7.8. $\exp : M_n(\mathbb{K}) \to M_n(\mathbb{K})$ *is smooth.*

This fact allows us to verify part (2) of Theorem 7.1 in the special case $G = GL_n(\mathbb{K})$. Remember that $B_r := \{W \in M_n(\mathbb{K}) \mid |W| < r\}$.

Lemma 7.9. *For sufficiently small $r > 0$, $V := \exp(B_r)$ is a neighborhood of I in $GL_n(\mathbb{K})$, and $\exp : B_r \to V$ is a homeomorphism (which is smooth and has smooth inverse).*

Proof. For all $X \in M_n(\mathbb{K})$, $d(\exp)_0(X)$ is the initial tangent vector to the path $t \mapsto e^{tX}$, namely X. In other words, $d(\exp)_0$ is the identity map. The result now follows from the inverse function theorem, together with the observation that a sufficiently small neighborhood of I in $M_n(\mathbb{K})$ must lie in $GL_n(\mathbb{K})$. $\qquad\square$

The inverse of $\exp$ is denoted "log"; it is a smooth function defined on a neighborhood of I in $GL_n(\mathbb{K})$. Although we will not require this fact, it is not hard to prove that $\log(A)$ equals the familiar power series for log evaluated on A:

$$\log(A) = (A-I) - (1/2)(A-I)^2 + (1/3)(A-I)^3 - (1/4)(A-I)^4 + \cdots .$$

Now let $G \subset GL_n(\mathbb{K})$ be a matrix group with Lie algebra $\mathfrak{g}$. Part 2 of Proposition 7.1 says that for sufficiently small $r > 0$, $\exp(B_r \cap \mathfrak{g})$ is a neighborhood of I in G. Lemma 7.9 handled the case where G is all of $GL_n(\mathbb{K})$. Generalizing to arbitrary G is not as obvious as it might at first seem. In fact, the proposition can be false for a subgroup $G \subset GL_n(\mathbb{K})$ which is not closed, as the next example illustrates.

Example 7.10. *Let $\lambda \in \mathbb{R}$ be an irrational multiple of 2π, and define*

$$G := \left\{ g_t = \begin{pmatrix} e^{t\mathbf{i}} & 0 \\ 0 & e^{\lambda t\mathbf{i}} \end{pmatrix} \,\Big|\, t \in \mathbb{R} \right\} \subset GL_2(\mathbb{C}).$$

The Lie algebra of G is the span of $W = \begin{pmatrix} \mathbf{i} & 0 \\ 0 & \lambda\mathbf{i} \end{pmatrix}$, and $e^{tW} = g_t$ for all $t \in \mathbb{R}$. For $0 < r < \infty$, notice that

$$\exp(\{tW \mid t \in (-r,r)\}) = \{g_t \mid t \in (-r,r)\}$$

is not a neighborhood of I in G. Any neighborhood of I in G contains points of the form $g_{2\pi n}$ for arbitrarily large integers n; compare with Exercise 4.24.

We require the following important lemma:

Lemma 7.11. *Let $G \subset GL_n(\mathbb{K})$ be a matrix group with Lie algebra $\mathfrak{g}$. In Lemma 7.9, $r > 0$ can be chosen such that additionally:*

$$\exp(B_r \cap \mathfrak{g}) = \exp(B_r) \cap G.$$

For any r, $\exp(B_r \cap \mathfrak{g}) \subset \exp(B_r) \cap G$, so the real content of this lemma is that the other inclusion holds for sufficiently small r. The lemma is false for certain non-closed subgroups of $GL_n(\mathbb{K})$, including the one in Example 7.10. The essential problem is this: there are elements of G (namely $g_{2\pi n}$ for certain large n) which are arbitrarily close to I, so they are exponential images of arbitrarily short vectors in $M_n(\mathbb{K})$, but they are exponential images only of very long vectors in $\mathfrak{g}$.

Proof of Lemma 7.11. Choose a subspace $\mathfrak{p} \subset M_n(\mathbb{K})$ which is complementary to $\mathfrak{g}$, as in the proof of part (1) of Theorem 7.1, so $M_n(\mathbb{K}) = \mathfrak{g} \times \mathfrak{p}$. Define the function $\Phi : \mathfrak{g} \times \mathfrak{p} \to M_n(\mathbb{K})$ so that $\Phi(X + Y) = e^X e^Y$ for all $X \in \mathfrak{g}$ and $Y \in \mathfrak{p}$. Notice that Φ agrees with exp on $\mathfrak{g}$. The functions Φ and exp are also similar in that the derivative of each at 0 is the identity. In particular, Φ is locally invertible by the inverse function theorem.

Assume the lemma is false. Then there must be a sequence of non-zero vectors $\{A_1, A_2, ...\}$ in $M_n(\mathbb{K})$ with $|A_i| \to 0$ such that $A_i \notin \mathfrak{g}$ and $\Phi(A_i) \in G$ for all i. Write $A_i = X_i + Y_i$, where $X_i \in \mathfrak{g}$ and $0 \neq Y_i \in \mathfrak{p}$. For all i, let $g_i := \Phi(A_i) = e^{X_i} e^{Y_i} \in G$. Notice that $e^{Y_i} = (e^{X_i})^{-1} g_i \in G$.

By compactness of the sphere of unit-length vectors in $\mathfrak{p}$, the sequence $\{\frac{Y_1}{|Y_1|}, \frac{Y_2}{|Y_2|}, ...\}$ must sub-converge to some unit-length vector $Y \in \mathfrak{p}$ (by Proposition 4.24). For notational convenience, re-choose the A_i's above so that the sequence converges rather than sub-converges to Y.

Let $t \in \mathbb{R}$. Since $|Y_i| \to 0$, it is possible to choose a sequence of positive integers n_i such that $n_i Y_i \to tY$. Since $e^{n_i Y_i} = (e^{Y_i})^{n_i} \in G$, and since G is closed in $GL_n(\mathbb{K})$, it follows that $e^{tY} \in G$. In summary, $e^{tY} \in G$ for all $t \in \mathbb{R}$, which is impossible since $Y \notin \mathfrak{g}$. $\square$

Proof of part (2) of Theorem 7.1. Pick $r > 0$ as in Lemma 7.11. Then $V = \exp(B_r \cap \mathfrak{g})$ is a neighborhood of I in G because it equals the set $\exp(B_r) \cap G$, and $\exp(B_r)$ is open in $M_n(\mathbb{K})$ by Lemma 7.9. The restriction $\exp : B_r \cap \mathfrak{g} \to V$ is continuous. Its inverse function $\log : V \to B_r \cap \mathfrak{g}$ is continuous because it is a restriction of the continuous function $\log : \exp(B_r) \to B_r$. $\qquad\square$

In the previous proof, $\exp : B_r \cap \mathfrak{g} \to V$ is not only continuous, it is smooth. Its inverse $\log : V \to B_r \cap \mathfrak{g}$ is also better than continuous; it is the restriction to V of the smooth function $\log$.

4. Manifolds

In this section, we define manifolds and prove that matrix groups are manifolds.

Let $X \subset \mathbb{R}^m$ be any subset, and let $f : X \to \mathbb{R}^n$ be a function. If X is open, it makes sense to ask whether f is smooth. If X is not open, then the partial derivatives of f at $p \in X$ might not make sense, because f need not be defined near p in all coordinate directions. We will call f smooth if it locally extends to a smooth function on $\mathbb{R}^m$:

Definition 7.12. *If $X \subset \mathbb{R}^m$, then $f : X \to \mathbb{R}^n$ is called __smooth__ if for all $p \in X$, there exists a neighborhood U of p in $\mathbb{R}^m$ and a smooth function $\tilde{f} : U \to \mathbb{R}^n$ which agrees with f on $X \cap U$.*

This extended notion of smoothness allows us to define an important type of equivalence for subsets of Euclidean space:

Definition 7.13. *$X \subset \mathbb{R}^{m_1}$ and $Y \subset \mathbb{R}^{m_2}$ are called __diffeomorphic__ if there exists a smooth bijective function $f : X \to Y$ whose inverse is also smooth. In this case, f is called a __diffeomorphism__.*

From the discussion after its proof, it is clear that the word "homeomorphism" can be replaced by the word "diffeomorphism" in part (2) of Theorem 7.1.

A diffeomorphism is a homeomorphism which is smooth and has a smooth inverse. Figure 2 shows two sets which are homeomorphic but are not diffeomorphic, because no homeomorphism between them could be smooth at the cone point.

A manifold is a set which is locally diffeomorphic to Euclidean space:

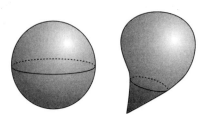

Figure 2. Homeomorphic but not diffeomorphic.

Definition 7.14. *A subset $X \subset \mathbb{R}^m$ is called a* manifold *of dimension n if for all $p \in X$ there exists a neighborhood V of p in X which is diffeomorphic to an open set $U \subset \mathbb{R}^n$.*

In Figure 2, the round sphere is a 2-dimensional manifold in $\mathbb{R}^3$. A sufficiently small and nearsighted bug living on this sphere would think it lived on $\mathbb{R}^2$. But the pointed sphere is not a manifold, since a bug living at the cone-point, no matter how nearsighted, could distinguish its home from $\mathbb{R}^2$.

Bugs are fine, but to rigorously prove that a set X is a manifold, you must construct a parametrization at every $p \in X$, meaning a diffeomorphism φ from an open set $U \subset \mathbb{R}^n$ to a neighborhood V of p in X, as in Figure 3.

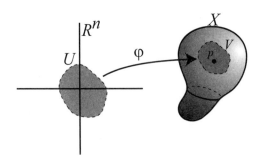

Figure 3. A parametrization of X at p.

For practice, we will prove $S^2 = \{(x, y, x) \in \mathbb{R}^3 \mid x^2 + y^2 + z^2 = 1\}$ is a 2-dimensional manifold.

Proposition 7.15. $S^2 \subset \mathbb{R}^3$ *is a 2-dimensional manifold.*

Proof. The upper hemisphere

$$V = \{(x, y, z) \in S^2 \mid z > 0\}$$

is a neighborhood of $(0, 0, 1)$ in S^2. Define

$$U = \{(x, y) \in \mathbb{R}^2 \mid x^2 + y^2 < 1\},$$

and define $\varphi : U \to V$ as $\varphi(x, y) = (x, y, \sqrt{1 - x^2 - y^2})$. Then φ is smooth and bijective. The inverse $\varphi^{-1} : V \to U$ has the formula $\varphi^{-1}(x, y, z) = (x, y)$. By Definition 7.12, φ^{-1} is smooth because it extends to the smooth function with this same formula defined on the open set $\{(x, y, z) \in \mathbb{R}^3 \mid z > 0\}$, or even on all of $\mathbb{R}^3$.

For arbitrary $p \in S^2$, the function $(R_A) \circ \varphi : U \to R_A(V)$ is a parametrization at p, assuming $A \in SO(3)$ is any matrix for which $R_A(0, 0, 1) = p$. $\qquad \square$

Before proving that all matrix groups are manifolds, we give a simple example:

Claim 7.16. *The matrix group*

$$T = \{ \, diag(e^{\mathrm{i}\theta}, e^{\mathrm{i}\phi}) \mid \theta, \phi \in [0, 2\pi) \} \subset GL_2(\mathbb{C})$$

is a 2-dimensional manifold in $M_2(\mathbb{C}) \cong \mathbb{C}^4 \cong \mathbb{R}^8$.

Proof. Making the identification $M_2(\mathbb{C}) \cong \mathbb{R}^8$ explicit, we write:

$$T = \{(\cos\theta, \sin\theta, 0, 0, 0, 0, \cos\phi, \sin\phi) \mid \theta, \phi \in [0, 2\pi)\} \subset \mathbb{R}^8.$$

The identity element of T is $p = (1, 0, 0, 0, 0, 0, 1, 0)$. To describe a parametrization of T at p, let $U = \{(\theta, \phi) \in \mathbb{R}^2 \mid -\pi/2 < \theta, \phi < \pi/2\}$ and define $\varphi : U \to T$ as $(\theta, \phi) \mapsto (\cos\theta, \sin\theta, 0, 0, 0, 0, \cos\phi, \sin\phi)$. This parametrization is clearly smooth and is bijective onto its image $V = \varphi(U)$. The inverse $\varphi^{-1} : V \to U$ is also smooth because it extends to the smooth function from an open set in $\mathbb{R}^8$ to U defined as follows:

$$(x_1, x_2, x_3, x_4, x_5, x_6, x_7, x_8) \mapsto (\arctan(x_2/x_1), \arctan(x_8/x_7)).$$

A parametrization at an arbitrary point of T is defined similarly. $\qquad \square$

In the previous claim, notice T is diffeomorphic to the manifold in $\mathbb{R}^4$ obtained by removing the four irrelevant components of $\mathbb{R}^8$. In fact, T is diffeomorphic to a manifold in $\mathbb{R}^3$, the <u>torus of revolution</u> obtained by revolving about the z-axis a circle in the yz-plane. Each point on this torus of revolution is described by a pair of angles: θ describes a point on the circle in the yz-plane, and ϕ describes how far that point rotates about the z-axis.

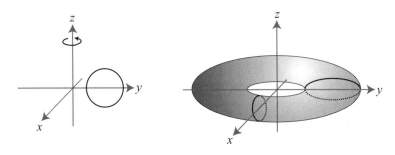

Figure 4. A torus of revolution in $\mathbb{R}^3$.

Theorem 7.17. *Any matrix group of dimension n is a manifold of dimension n.*

Proof. Let $G \subset GL_n(\mathbb{K})$ be a matrix group of dimension n with Lie algebra $\mathfrak{g}$. Choose $r > 0$ as in Theorem 7.1. Then $V = \exp(B_r \cap \mathfrak{g})$ is a neighborhood of I in G, and the restriction $\exp : B_r \cap \mathfrak{g} \to V$ is a parametrization at I. Here we are implicitly identifying $\mathfrak{g}$ with $\mathbb{R}^n$ by choosing a basis.

Next let $g \in G$ be arbitrary. Define $\mathcal{L}_g : M_n(\mathbb{K}) \to M_n(\mathbb{K})$ as

$$\mathcal{L}_g(A) := g \cdot A.$$

Notice that $\mathcal{L}_g$ restricts to a diffeomorphism from G to G. So $\mathcal{L}_g(V)$ is a neighborhood of g in G, and $(\mathcal{L}_g \circ \exp) : B_r \cap \mathfrak{g} \to \mathcal{L}_g(V)$ is a parametrization at g. $\square$

5. More about manifolds

In this section, we prove that each tangent space to a manifold is a subspace, and we define the "derivative" of a smooth function

$f : X_1 \to X_2$ between manifolds. The derivative of f at $p \in X_1$ will be denoted df_p and is a linear map from T_pX_1 to $T_{f(p)}X_2$. In future sections, our primary applications will be when f is a smooth homomorphism between matrix groups, in which case df_I is a linear map between their Lie algebras.

Remember that in Definition 5.1, the tangent space to a subset $X \subset \mathbb{R}^m$ at $p \in X$ was defined as:

$$T_pX := \{\gamma'(0) \mid \gamma : (-\epsilon, \epsilon) \to X \text{ is differentiable with } \gamma(0) = p\}.$$

Proposition 7.18. *If $X \subset \mathbb{R}^m$ is an n-dimensional manifold, then for all $p \in X$, T_pX is an n-dimensional subspace of $\mathbb{R}^m$.*

Proof. To prove the proposition, we will present a more technical definition of T_pX and then prove that the two definitions are equivalent. Let $\varphi : U \subset \mathbb{R}^n \to V \subset X$ be a parametrization at p. Assume for simplicity that $0 \in U$ and $\varphi(0) = p$. Define

$$T_pX := d\varphi_0(\mathbb{R}^n).$$

This makes sense if φ is regarded as a function from $U \subset \mathbb{R}^n$ to $\mathbb{R}^m$. Clearly T_pX is a subspace, since it's the image of a linear map. The two definitions of T_pX agree because differentiable paths through p in X are exactly the images under φ of differentiable paths in U through 0. In particular, this agreement shows that the technical definition of T_pX is well-defined; it does not depend on the choice of parametrization, φ. $\qquad\square$

Next we define the derivative of a function between manifolds. The definition is analogous to Proposition 7.5 and is pictured in Figure 5.

Definition 7.19. *Let $f : X_1 \to X_2$ be a smooth function between manifolds, and let $p \in X_1$. If $v \in T_pX_1$, then $df_p(v) \in T_{f(p)}X_2$ denotes the initial velocity vector $(f \circ \gamma)'(0)$ of the image under f of any differentiable path $\gamma(t)$ in X_1 with $\gamma(0) = p$ and $\gamma'(0) = v$.*

Proposition 7.20. *Under the hypotheses of Definition 7.19, the map $v \mapsto df_p(v)$ is a well-defined linear function from T_pX_1 to $T_{f(p)}X_2$.*

Here "well-defined" means independent of the choice of γ.

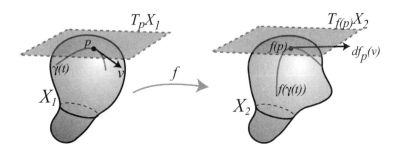

Figure 5. $df_p(v)$ means the initial velocity vector of the image
under f of a path γ in the direction of v.

Proof. To prove this proposition, we present a more technical definition of df_p and then prove that the two definitions are equivalent.

Let $\varphi_1 : U_1 \subset \mathbb{R}^{n_1} \to V_1 \subset X_1$ be a parametrization at p with $\varphi_1(0) = p$. Let $\varphi_2 : U_2 \subset \mathbb{R}^{n_2} \to V_2 \subset X_2$ be a parametrization at $f(p)$ with $\varphi_2(0) = f(p)$. The fact that f is smooth implies that

$$\phi := \varphi_2^{-1} \circ f \circ \varphi_1 : U_1 \to U_2$$

is smooth (one may have to shrink U_1 to a smaller neighborhood of 0 in $\mathbb{R}^{n_1}$ in order for ϕ to be defined on U_1). See Figure 6.

We define:

$$df_p := d(\varphi_2)_0 \circ d\phi_0 \circ (d(\varphi_1)_0)^{-1} : T_pX_1 \to T_{f(p)}X_2.$$

It is clear from this definition that df_p is linear, since it is the composition of three linear maps. For a fixed choice of the parameterizations φ_1 and φ_2, notice that this technical definition of df_p agrees with Definition 7.19. In particular, this shows that Definition 7.19 is well-defined (independent of choice of γ), which in turn shows that the technical definition is well-defined (independent of choices of parameterizations). $\qquad \square$

The two most important facts about derivatives of functions between Euclidean spaces generalize to functions between manifolds:

Proposition 7.21 (Chain rule for manifolds). *Suppose $f : X_1 \to X_2$ and $g : X_2 \to X_3$ are smooth functions between manifolds. Then so*

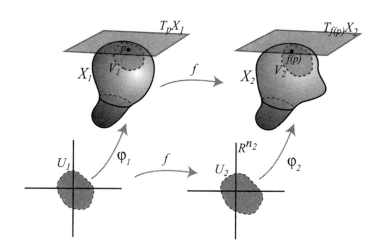

Figure 6. The technical definition of derivative.

is their composition, and for all $p \in X_1$,

$$d(g \circ f)_p = dg_{f(p)} \circ df_p.$$

Theorem 7.22 (Inverse function theorem for manifolds). *Suppose* $f : X_1 \to X_2$ *is a smooth function between manifolds, and* $p \in X_1$. *If* df_p *is an invertible linear map, then there exists a neighborhood* U *of* p *in* X_1 *such that* $V := f(U)$ *is a neighborhood of* $f(p)$ *in* X_2, *and the restriction* $f : U \to V$ *is a diffeomorphism. In particular,* X_1 *and* X_2 *must have the same dimension.*

We will consider matrix groups G_1 and G_2 equivalent if there exists a group-isomorphism $f : G_1 \to G_2$ which is also a diffeomorphism (so they simultaneously look the same as groups and as manifolds). In this case G_1 and G_2 will be called <u>smoothly isomorphic</u>. Dimension is a useful invariant of smooth isomorphism, which means that smoothly isomorphic matrix groups have the same dimension.

There is a non-trivial theorem which states that any continuous homomorphism between matrix groups is smooth. Therefore, "continuously isomorphic" is the same as "smoothly isomorphic"; see [**12**] or [13] for a proof. On the other hand, it is possible for a homomorphism between matrix groups to be discontinuous. For example, the additive group $(\mathbb{R}, +)$ can be considered a matrix group, because it is isomorphic to $\text{Trans}(\mathbb{R}^1)$. There are many discontinuous isomorphisms $f : (\mathbb{R}, +) \to (\mathbb{R}, +)$. In fact, any bijection of a basis for $\mathbb{R}$ (regarded as a vector space over $\mathbb{Q}$) extends linearly to an isomorphism.

6. Exercises

Ex. 7.1. Prove that $S^n \subset \mathbb{R}^{n+1}$ is an n-dimensional manifold.

Ex. 7.2. Prove that the cone $\{(x, y, z) \in \mathbb{R}^3 \mid z = \sqrt{x^2 + y^2}\} \subset \mathbb{R}^3$ is not a manifold.

Ex. 7.3. If $X_1 \in \mathbb{R}^{m_1}$ and $X_2 \in \mathbb{R}^{m_2}$ are manifolds whose dimensions are d_1 and d_2, prove that

$$X_1 \times X_2 = \{(p_1, p_2) \in \mathbb{R}^{m_1} \times \mathbb{R}^{m_2} \cong \mathbb{R}^{m_1+m_2} \mid p_1 \in X_1, p_2 \in X_2\}$$

is a $d_1 + d_2$ dimensional manifold.

Ex. 7.4. Is the group G in Example 7.10 a manifold?

Ex. 7.5. Let $f : \mathbb{R}^m \to \mathbb{R}^n$ be a *linear* function. For any $p \in \mathbb{R}^m$, show that $df_p = f$. In other words, the derivative of a linear function is itself.

Ex. 7.6. Let G be a (not necessarily path-connected) matrix group. Define the identity component, G_0, of G as:

$$\{g \in G \mid \exists \text{ continuous } \gamma : [0, 1] \to G \text{ with } \gamma(0) = I \text{ and } \gamma(1) = g\}.$$

Prove that G^0 is a matrix group (don't forget to prove G^0 is closed). Prove that G^0 is a normal subgroup of G.

Ex. 7.7. Prove that there exists a neighborhood of I in $GL_n(\mathbb{K})$ which does not contain any subgroup of $GL_n(\mathbb{K})$ other than $\{I\}$.

Ex. 7.8. Prove the chain rule for manifolds.

Ex. 7.9. Prove the inverse function theorem for manifolds.

Ex. 7.10. Let X be a manifold. If X contains no clopen subsets other than itself and the empty set, prove that X is path-connected (this is a converse of Proposition 4.18 for manifolds).

Ex. 7.11. Let $X \subset \mathbb{R}^m$ be a manifold. Define the <u>tangent bundle</u> of X as:

$$TX := \{(p,v) \in \mathbb{R}^m \times \mathbb{R}^m \cong \mathbb{R}^{2m} \mid p \in X \text{ and } v \in T_pX\}.$$

Prove that TX is a manifold of dimension twice the dimension of X.

Ex. 7.12. If $X \subset \mathbb{R}^m$ is a manifold, define the <u>unit tangent bundle</u> of X as:

$$T^1X := \{(p,v) \in \mathbb{R}^m \times \mathbb{R}^m \cong \mathbb{R}^{2m} \mid p \in X \text{ and } v \in T_pX \text{ and } |v| = 1\}.$$

Prove that T^1X is a manifold of dimension one less than the dimension of TX.

Ex. 7.13. Describe a diffeomorphism between $SO(3)$ and T^1S^2 (compare to Exercise 1.1).

Ex. 7.14. Let $f : \mathbb{R}^n \to \mathbb{R}^n$ ($n \geq 2$) be a diffeomorphism which sends lines to lines, in the sense of Exercise 3.11. Prove that f has the formula $f(X) = R_A(X) + V$ for some $A \in GL_n(\mathbb{R})$ and some $V \in \mathbb{R}^n$; in other words f is represented by an element of $\mathrm{Aff}_n(\mathbb{R})$. *Hint: First prove that the matrix df_p is independent of the choice of $p \in \mathbb{R}^n$.*

Ex. 7.15. Let G_1 and G_2 be matrix groups with Lie algebras $\mathfrak{g}_1$ and $\mathfrak{g}_2$. Let $f : G_1 \to G_2$ be a C^1 homomorphism. Notice that $df_I : \mathfrak{g}_1 \to \mathfrak{g}_2$. Prove that for all $v \in \mathfrak{g}_1$,

$$f(e^v) = e^{df_I(v)}.$$

In other words, a C^1 homomorphism is completely determined by its derivative at the identity, at least in a neighborhood of the identity. *Hint: Use Proposition 6.17.* Conclude that any C^1 homomorphism is smooth, at least in a neighborhood of the identity.

Ex. 7.16. Let $X \subset \mathbb{R}^m$ be a manifold. Let $f : X \to \mathbb{R}$ be a smooth function. Define the <u>graph</u> of f as:

$$\Lambda := \{(p,t) \in \mathbb{R}^m \times \mathbb{R} \cong \mathbb{R}^{m+1} \mid p \in X \text{ and } f(p) = t\}.$$

Prove that Λ is a manifold.

Chapter 8

The Lie bracket

Since dimension is the only invariant of vector spaces, any two matrix groups of the same dimension have Lie algebras which are isomorphic as vector spaces. So how can we justify our previous assertion that the Lie algebra $\mathfrak{g}$ encodes a surprising amount of information about the matrix group G? In this chapter, we define the "Lie bracket" operation on $\mathfrak{g}$. For vectors $A, B \in \mathfrak{g}$, the Lie bracket $[A, B] \in \mathfrak{g}$ encodes information about the products of elements of G in the directions of A and B. Together with its Lie bracket operation, $\mathfrak{g}$ encodes information about what G looks like near the identity, not just as a manifold, but also as a group. We define Lie brackets in terms of the *adjoint action*. We also use the adjoint action in this chapter to construct a fundamental 2-to-1 smooth homomorphism from $Sp(1)$ to $SO(3)$.

1. The Lie bracket

Let G be a matrix group with Lie algebra $\mathfrak{g}$. For all $g \in G$, the conjugation map $C_g : G \to G$, defined as

$$C_g(a) := gag^{-1},$$

is a smooth isomorphism. The derivative $d(C_g)_I : \mathfrak{g} \to \mathfrak{g}$ is a vector space isomorphism, which we denote as Ad_g:

$$\mathrm{Ad}_g := d(C_g)_I.$$

To derive a simple formula for $Ad_g(B)$, notice that any $B \in \mathfrak{g}$ can be represented as $B = b'(0)$, where $b(t)$ is a differentiable path in G with $b(0) = I$. The product rule gives:

$$\mathrm{Ad}_g(B) = d(C_g)_I(B) = \left.\frac{d}{dt}\right|_{t=0} gb(t)g^{-1} = gBg^{-1}.$$

So we learn that:

$$Ad_g(B) = gBg^{-1}.$$

If all elements of G commute with g, then Ad_g is the identity map on $\mathfrak{g}$. So in general, Ad_g measures the failure of g to commute with elements of G near I. More specifically, $Ad_g(B)$ measures the failure of g to commute with elements of G near I in the direction of B. Investigating this phenomena when g is itself close to I leads one to define:

Definition 8.1. *The Lie bracket of two vectors A and B in $\mathfrak{g}$ is:*

$$[A, B] = \left.\frac{d}{dt}\right|_{t=0} Ad_{a(t)}B,$$

where $a(t)$ is any differentiable path in G with $a(0) = I$ and $a'(0) = A$.

Notice $[A, B] \in \mathfrak{g}$, since it is the initial velocity vector of a path in $\mathfrak{g}$. It measures the failure of elements of G near I in the direction of A to commute with elements of G near I in the direction of B. The following alternative definition is easier to calculate and verifies that Definition 8.1 is independent of the choice of path $a(t)$.

Proposition 8.2. *For all $A, B \in \mathfrak{g}$, $[A, B] = AB - BA$.*

Proof. Let $a(t)$ and $b(t)$ be differentiable paths in G with $a(0) = I$, $b(0) = I$, $a'(0) = A$ and $b'(0) = B$. Using the product rule and Equation 5.1:

$$[A, B] = \left.\frac{d}{dt}\right|_{t=0} a(t)Ba(t)^{-1} = AB - BA.$$

$\square$

Notice $[A, B] = 0$ if and only if A and B commute. The commutativity of A and B reflects the commutativity of elements of G in the directions of A and B. One precise way to formulate this is:

Proposition 8.3. *Let $A, B \in \mathfrak{g}$.*

(1) *If $[A, B] = 0$, then e^{tA} commutes with e^{sB} for all $t, s \in \mathbb{R}$.*

(2) *If e^{tA} and e^{sB} commute for $t, s \in (-\epsilon, \epsilon)$, then $[A, B] = 0$.*

Proof. For (1), if A and B commute, then

$$e^{tA}e^{sB} = e^{tA+sB} = e^{sB+tA} = e^{sB}e^{tA}.$$

For (2), fix $t \in (-\epsilon, \epsilon)$, and notice that

$$Ad_{(e^{tA})}B = e^{tA}Be^{-tA} = \frac{d}{ds}\Big|_{s=0} e^{tA}e^{sB}e^{-tA} = \frac{d}{ds}\Big|_{s=0} e^{sB} = B,$$

which implies that $[A, B] = 0$. □

The following properties of the Lie bracket follow immediately from Proposition 8.2:

Proposition 8.4. *For all $A, A_1, A_2, B, B_1, B_2, C \in \mathfrak{g}$ and $\lambda_1, \lambda_2 \in \mathbb{R}$,*

(1) $[\lambda_1 A_1 + \lambda_2 A_2, B] = \lambda_1[A_1, B] + \lambda_2[A_2, B]$.

(2) $[A, \lambda_1 B_1 + \lambda_2 B_2] = \lambda_1[A, B_1] + \lambda_2[A, B_2]$.

(3) $[A, B] = -[B, A]$.

(4) *(Jacobi identity)* $[[A, B], C] + [[B, C], A] + [[C, A], B] = 0$.

The group operation in G determines the Lie bracket operation in $\mathfrak{g}$. One therefore expects smoothly isomorphic groups to have isomorphic Lie algebras. Before proving this, we need to precisely define "isomorphic Lie algebras".

Definition 8.5. *Let $\mathfrak{g}_1$ and $\mathfrak{g}_2$ be two Lie algebras. A linear function $f : \mathfrak{g}_1 \to \mathfrak{g}_2$ is called a <u>Lie algebra homomorphism</u> if for all $A, B \in \mathfrak{g}_1$,*

$$f([A, B]) = [f(A), f(B)].$$

If f is also bijective, then f is called a <u>Lie algebra isomorphism</u>.

The most important Lie algebra homomorphisms are the ones determined by smooth group homomorphisms.

Proposition 8.6. *Let G_1, G_2 be matrix groups with Lie algebras $\mathfrak{g}_1, \mathfrak{g}_2$. Let $f : G_1 \to G_2$ be a smooth homomorphism. Then the derivative $df_I : \mathfrak{g}_1 \to \mathfrak{g}_2$ is a Lie algebra homomorphism.*

Proof. Let $A, B \in \mathfrak{g}_1$. Let $a(t)$ and $b(t)$ be differentiable paths with $a(0) = b(0) = I$, $a'(0) = A$ and $b'(0) = B$. For all $a \in G_1$, we will first show:

$$(8.1) \qquad df_I(\mathrm{Ad}_a(B)) = \mathrm{Ad}_{f(a)}(df_I(B)).$$

Since $\alpha(t) = ab(t)a^{-1}$ satisfies $\alpha(0) = I$ and $\alpha'(0) = \mathrm{Ad}_a(B)$, Equation 8.1 can be justified as follows:

$$\begin{aligned}
df_I(\mathrm{Ad}_a(B)) &= \frac{d}{dt}\Big|_{t=0}(f \circ \alpha)(t) = \frac{d}{dt}\Big|_{t=0} f(ab(t)a^{-1}) \\
&= \frac{d}{dt}\Big|_{t=0} f(a)f(b(t))f(a)^{-1} = \mathrm{Ad}_{f(a)}(df_I(B)).
\end{aligned}$$

Finally, apply Equation 8.1 to $a = a(t)$ as follows:

$$\begin{aligned}
df_I([A, B]) &= df_I\left(\frac{d}{dt}\Big|_{t=0}\mathrm{Ad}_{a(t)}B\right) = \frac{d}{dt}\Big|_{t=0}df_I(\mathrm{Ad}_{a(t)}B) \\
&= \frac{d}{dt}\Big|_{t=0}\mathrm{Ad}_{f(a(t))}(df_I(B)) = [df_I(A), df_I(B)].
\end{aligned}$$

The second equality above implicitly uses that, since $df_I : \mathfrak{g}_1 \to \mathfrak{g}_2$ is linear, its derivative at any point of $\mathfrak{g}_1$ is itself (see Exercise 7.5). So, since $v(t) := \mathrm{Ad}_{a(t)}B$ is a path in $\mathfrak{g}_1$, this second equality is justified by:

$$df_I(v'(0)) = d(df_I)_{v(0)}(v'(0)) = \frac{d}{dt}\Big|_{t=0}df_I(v(t)).$$

$\square$

Corollary 8.7. *Smoothly isomorphic matrix groups have isomorphic Lie algebras.*

Proof. Suppose that $f : G_1 \to G_2$ is a smooth isomorphism between two matrix groups. Then $df_I : \mathfrak{g}_1 \to \mathfrak{g}_2$ is a Lie algebra homomorphism. Further, df_I is bijective, as is justified by the discussion preceding Theorem 7.6. Thus, df_I is a Lie algebra isomorphism. $\square$

Several familiar 3-dimensional matrix groups have isomorphic Lie algebras:

(8.2)

$$so(3) = \text{span}\left\{\begin{pmatrix} 0 & 0 & 0 \\ 0 & 0 & -1 \\ 0 & 1 & 0 \end{pmatrix}, \begin{pmatrix} 0 & 0 & 1 \\ 0 & 0 & 0 \\ -1 & 0 & 0 \end{pmatrix}, \begin{pmatrix} 0 & -1 & 0 \\ 1 & 0 & 0 \\ 0 & 0 & 0 \end{pmatrix}\right\}.$$

$$su(2) = \text{span}\left\{\frac{1}{2}\begin{pmatrix} 0 & 1 \\ -1 & 0 \end{pmatrix}, \frac{1}{2}\begin{pmatrix} i & 0 \\ 0 & -i \end{pmatrix}, \frac{1}{2}\begin{pmatrix} 0 & i \\ i & 0 \end{pmatrix}\right\}.$$

$$sp(1) = \text{span}\left\{\frac{1}{2}(\mathbf{i}), \frac{1}{2}(\mathbf{j}), \frac{1}{2}(\mathbf{k})\right\}.$$

In all three, for the given basis $\{A_1, A_2, A_3\}$, it is straightforward to check:

$$[A_1, A_2] = A_3, \quad [A_2, A_3] = A_1, \quad [A_3, A_1] = A_2.$$

So all three Lie algebras have the same Lie bracket structure, or more precisely, the linear map between two of them which sends basis elements to corresponding basis elements is a Lie algebra isomorphism. If these bases are used to identify the Lie algebras with $\mathbb{R}^3$, notice that the Lie bracket operation becomes the familiar cross product from vector calculus.

The fact that $su(2) \cong sp(1)$ is not surprising, since $SU(2)$ and $Sp(1)$ are smoothly isomorphic (by Proposition 3.13). We will later learn that $SO(3)$ is neither isomorphic nor homeomorphic to $Sp(1)$, in spite of the fact that their Lie algebras look identical. Another such example is the pair $SO(n)$ and $O(n)$, which have identical Lie algebras but are not isomorphic. It turns out that path-connected, *simply connected* matrix groups are smoothly isomorphic if and only if their Lie algebras are isomorphic. It is beyond the scope of this text to precisely define "simply connected" or prove this fact.

2. The adjoint action

Let $G \subset GL_n(\mathbb{K})$ be a matrix group of dimension d, with Lie algebra $\mathfrak{g}$. For every $g \in G$, $\text{Ad}_g : \mathfrak{g} \to \mathfrak{g}$ is a vector space isomorphism. Once we choose a basis $\mathcal{B}$ of $\mathfrak{g}$, this isomorphism can be represented as L_A for some $A \in GL_d(\mathbb{R})$, as in Section 1.7. In other words, after fixing a basis of $\mathfrak{g}$, we can regard the map $g \mapsto \mathrm{Ad}_g$ as a function from G to $GL_d(\mathbb{R})$.

Lemma 8.8. $Ad : G \to GL_d(\mathbb{R})$ *is a smooth homomorphism.*

Proof. For all $g_1, g_2 \in G$ and all $X \in \mathfrak{g}$,

$$\mathrm{Ad}_{g_1 g_2}(X) = (g_1 g_2) X (g_1 g_2)^{-1} = g_1 g_2 X g_2^{-1} g_1^{-1} = \mathrm{Ad}_{g_1}(\mathrm{Ad}_{g_2}(X)).$$

This shows that $\mathrm{Ad}_{g_1 g_2} = \mathrm{Ad}_{g_1} \circ \mathrm{Ad}_{g_2}$. Since the composition of two linear maps corresponds to the product of the matrices representing them, this verifies that $\mathrm{Ad} : G \to GL_d(\mathbb{R})$ is a homomorphism. We leave to the reader (in Exercise 8.11) the straightforward verification that Ad is smooth. $\qquad\square$

This homomorphism is called the adjoint action of G on $\mathfrak{g}$. In general, an action of a matrix group G on a Euclidean space $\mathbb{R}^m$ means a homomorphism from G to $GL_m(\mathbb{R})$. It associates each element of G with a linear transformation of $\mathbb{R}^m$, and hence determines how elements of G "act on" vectors in $\mathbb{R}^m$. For example, we have studied all along how $SO(n)$ acts on $\mathbb{R}^n$; it is interesting that $SO(n)$ also acts naturally on $so(n) \cong \mathbb{R}^{n(n-1)/2}$.

The image of Ad in $GL_d(\mathbb{R})$ contains only Lie algebra isomorphims, since:

Lemma 8.9. *For all $g \in G$ and all $X, Y \in \mathfrak{g}$,*

$$[Ad_g(X), Ad_g(Y)] = Ad_g([X, Y]).$$

Proof. This follows from Proposition 8.6, since $\mathrm{Ad}_g = d(C_g)_I$. An alternative proof is the following explicit verification:

$$
\begin{aligned}
[\mathrm{Ad}_g(X), \mathrm{Ad}_g(Y)] &= [gXg^{-1}, gYg^{-1}] \\
&= gXg^{-1}gYg^{-1} - gYg^{-1}gXg^{-1} \\
&= g(XY - YX)g^{-1} \\
&= \mathrm{Ad}_g([X, Y]).
\end{aligned}
$$

$\qquad\square$

The fact that $\mathrm{Ad} : G \to GL_d(\mathbb{R})$ is a smooth homomorphism has a very strong consequence; namely, Ad sends one-parameter groups in

G to one-parameter groups in $GL_d(\mathbb{R})$. To elaborate on this comment, for any $X \in \mathfrak{g}$, we denote by

$$\mathrm{ad}_X : \mathfrak{g} \to \mathfrak{g}$$

the linear map which sends Y to $[X, Y]$. That is, $\mathrm{ad}_X(Y) := [X, Y]$.

Proposition 8.10. *For all $X \in \mathfrak{g}$, $Ad_{e^X} = e^{\mathrm{ad}_X}$.*

Before proving this proposition, we explain it. On the right side, exponentiation of the linear map $\mathrm{ad}_X : \mathfrak{g} \to \mathfrak{g}$ is defined as follows. In our fixed basis, $\mathcal{B}$, of $\mathfrak{g}$, ad_X is represented by a matrix. This matrix can be exponentiated, and the linear transformation $\mathfrak{g} \to \mathfrak{g}$ associated to the result is denoted e^{ad_X}. The result is independent of the choice of $\mathcal{B}$ by Proposition 6.18. In fact, e^{ad_X} can be computed by formally substituting ad_X into the exponential power series. That is, for all $Y \in \mathfrak{g}$,

$$(e^{\mathrm{ad}_X})(Y) = (I + (\mathrm{ad}_X) + (1/2)(\mathrm{ad}_X)^2 + (1/6)(\mathrm{ad}_X)^3 + \cdots)Y$$
$$= Y + [X, Y] + (1/2)[X, [X, Y]] + (1/6)[X, [X, [X, Y]]] + \cdots.$$

So the theorem says that the transformation $\mathrm{Ad}_g : \mathfrak{g} \to \mathfrak{g}$ (when $g = e^X$) can be calculated purely in terms of repeated Lie brackets with X.

Proof. The key is that for $X \in \mathfrak{g}$, $d(\mathrm{Ad})_I(X) \in gl_d(\mathbb{R})$ is the matrix representing ad_X. We abbreviate this as:

$$(8.3) \qquad d(\mathrm{Ad})_I(X) = \mathrm{ad}_X.$$

Equation 8.3 follows immediately from Definition 8.1, or more explicitly by observing that for all $Y \in \mathfrak{g}$:

(8.4)
$$\frac{d}{dt}\bigg|_{t=0} \mathrm{Ad}_{e^{tX}}(Y) = \frac{d}{dt}\bigg|_{t=0}(e^{tX}Ye^{-tX}) = XY - YX = \mathrm{ad}_X(Y).$$

Now, $\mathrm{Ad} : G \to GL_d(\mathbb{R})$ is a smooth homomorphism. By Exercise 7.15, a smooth homomorphism between matrix groups sends one-parameter groups to one-parameter groups and is therefore completely determined by its derivative at I. More precisely, for all $X \in \mathfrak{g}$,

$$\mathrm{Ad}_{e^X} = e^{d(\mathrm{Ad})_I(X)} = e^{\mathrm{ad}_X}.$$

$\square$

3. Example: the adjoint action for $SO(3)$

In this section, we explicitly compute the adjoint action for $SO(3)$. For this purpose, a convenient choice of basis of $so(3)$ is:

$$\left\{ E_1 = \begin{pmatrix} 0 & 0 & 0 \\ 0 & 0 & -1 \\ 0 & 1 & 0 \end{pmatrix}, E_2 = \begin{pmatrix} 0 & 0 & 1 \\ 0 & 0 & 0 \\ -1 & 0 & 0 \end{pmatrix}, E_3 = \begin{pmatrix} 0 & -1 & 0 \\ 1 & 0 & 0 \\ 0 & 0 & 0 \end{pmatrix} \right\}.$$

As mentioned in Equation 8.2, the Lie bracket structure is:

$$[E_1, E_2] = E_3, \quad [E_2, E_3] = E_1, \quad [E_3, E_1] = E_2.$$

This basis determines a vector space isomorphism $f : \mathbb{R}^3 \to so(3)$, namely,

$$(a, b, c) \xmapsto{f} \begin{pmatrix} 0 & -c & b \\ c & 0 & -a \\ -b & a & 0 \end{pmatrix}.$$

For every $g \in SO(3)$, $\mathrm{Ad}_g : so(3) \to so(3)$ can be regarded (via f) as a linear map $\mathbb{R}^3 \to \mathbb{R}^3$, which equals left-multiplication by some matrix. We carefully chose the basis above such that this matrix will turn out to be g. In other words, conjugating an element of $so(3)$ by g gives the same answer as left-multiplying the corresponding vector in $\mathbb{R}^3$ by g:

(8.5) $$g(f(a, b, c))g^{-1} = f(g \cdot (a, b, c)).$$

Equation 8.5 is equivalent to the following proposition:

Proposition 8.11. *In the above basis, $Ad : SO(3) \to GL_3(\mathbb{R})$ is just the inclusion map, which sends every matrix to itself.*

Proof. We first show that the derivative $d(\mathrm{Ad})_I : so(3) \to gl_3(\mathbb{R})$ sends every matrix to itself. Let $\gamma(t)$ be a path in $SO(3)$ with $\gamma(0) = I$ and $\gamma'(0) = E_1$. Let $v \in so(3)$. Then $t \mapsto \mathrm{Ad}_{\gamma(t)}(v)$ is a path in $so(3)$

whose derivative equals (as in Equation 8.4):

$$\frac{d}{dt}\Big|_{t=0} \mathrm{Ad}_{\gamma(t)}(v) = \frac{d}{dt}\Big|_{t=0} \gamma(t)v\gamma(t)^{-1}$$

$$= E_1 v - v E_1 = [E_1, v] = \begin{cases} 0 \text{ if } v = E_1 \\ E_3 \text{ if } v = E_2 \\ -E_2 \text{ if } v = E_3 \end{cases} = f(E_1 \cdot f^{-1}(v)).$$

Thus, the linear transformation

$$v \mapsto \frac{d}{dt}\Big|_{t=0} \mathrm{Ad}_{\gamma(t)}(v)$$

is represented in this basis as left multiplication by the matrix E_1. This shows that $d(\mathrm{Ad})_I(E_1) = E_1$. A similar argument gives that $d(\mathrm{Ad})_I(E_2) = E_2$ and $d(\mathrm{Ad})_I(E_3) = E_3$. Thus, $d(\mathrm{Ad})_I$ sends every matrix in $so(3)$ to itself.

Since $d(\mathrm{Ad})_I$ sends every matrix to itself, $\mathrm{Ad} : SO(3) \to GL_3(\mathbb{R})$ sends every one-parameter group in $SO(3)$ to itself. We will prove in the next chapter that $\exp : so(3) \to SO(3)$ is surjective, so every element of $SO(3)$ is contained in a one-parameter-group. To conclude the proof without using this fact, one can verify that the set of all $g \in SO(3)$ sent to themselves by Ad is clopen, and hence is all of $SO(3)$. $\square$

4. The adjoint action for compact matrix groups

We saw that the image of Ad in $GL_d(\mathbb{R})$ contains only Lie algebra isomorphisms. A second important restriction on the image of Ad in $GL_d(\mathbb{R})$ applies only when G is a subgroup of $O(n)$, $U(n)$ or $Sp(n)$:

Proposition 8.12. *If G is a subgroup of $\mathcal{O}_n(\mathbb{K})$, then for all $g \in G$ and all $X \in \mathfrak{g}$, $|Ad_g(X)| = |X|$.*

Remember that $|\cdot|$ denotes the restriction to $\mathfrak{g}$ of the Euclidean norm on $M_n(\mathbb{K})$ regarded as $\mathbb{R}^{n^2}$, $\mathbb{R}^{2n^2}$ or $\mathbb{R}^{4n^2}$. For example, in $u(2)$,

$$\left| \begin{pmatrix} a\mathbf{i} & b+c\mathbf{i} \\ -b+c\mathbf{i} & d\mathbf{i} \end{pmatrix} \right| = \sqrt{a^2 + 2b^2 + 2c^2 + d^2}.$$

Proof. For $X, Y \in M_n(\mathbb{K}) \cong \mathbb{K}^{n^2}$, a convenient alternative description of their inner product, $\langle X, Y \rangle_\mathbb{K}$, is:

$$(8.6) \qquad \langle X, Y \rangle_\mathbb{K} = \mathrm{trace}(X \cdot Y^*).$$

Equation 8.6 is justified as follows:

$$\mathrm{trace}(X \cdot Y^*) = \sum_{i=1}^n (X \cdot Y^*)_{ii} = \sum_{i=1}^n \sum_{j=1}^n X_{ij}(Y^*)_{ji}$$

$$= \sum_{i,j=1}^n X_{ij}\overline{Y}_{ij} = \langle X, Y \rangle_\mathbb{K}.$$

We will use this alternative description to prove that for all $g \in \mathcal{O}_n(\mathbb{K})$ and all $X \in M_n(\mathbb{K})$,

$$(8.7) \qquad |Xg| = |gX| = |X|.$$

To justify Equation 8.7, we use the fact that $g \cdot g^* = I$:

$$|Xg|^2 = \mathrm{trace}((Xg)(Xg)^*) = \mathrm{trace}(Xgg^*X^*) = \mathrm{trace}(XX^*) = |X|^2.$$

For the other half:

$$|gX|^2 = |(gX)^*|^2 = \mathrm{trace}((gX)^*(gX)) = \mathrm{trace}(X^*g^*gX)$$

$$= \mathrm{trace}(X^*X) = |X^*|^2 = |X|^2.$$

The proposition follows immediately, since $|gXg^{-1}| = |gX| = |X|$. $\qquad\square$

Since $\mathfrak{g}$ is only an $\mathbb{R}$-subspace of $M_n(\mathbb{K}) \cong \mathbb{K}^{n^2}$ (not necessarily a $\mathbb{K}$-subspace), we will consider only the *real* part of the $\mathbb{K}$-inner product $\langle \cdot, \cdot \rangle_\mathbb{K}$ on $\mathfrak{g} \subset M_n(\mathbb{K})$. This is the same as regarding $M_n(\mathbb{K})$ as $\mathbb{R}^{n^2}$, $\mathbb{R}^{2n^2}$ or $\mathbb{R}^{4n^2}$, and restricting the $\mathbb{R}$-inner product $\langle \cdot, \cdot \rangle_\mathbb{R}$ to $\mathfrak{g}$. For example, in $u(2)$,

$$\left\langle \begin{pmatrix} a_1\mathbf{i} & b_1 + c_1\mathbf{i} \\ -b_1 + c_1\mathbf{i} & d_1\mathbf{i} \end{pmatrix}, \begin{pmatrix} a_2\mathbf{i} & b_2 + c_2\mathbf{i} \\ -b_2 + c_2\mathbf{i} & d_2\mathbf{i} \end{pmatrix} \right\rangle_\mathbb{R}$$

$$= a_1a_2 + 2b_1b_2 + 2c_1c_2 + d_1d_2.$$

Assume that G is a subgroup of $\mathcal{O}_n(\mathbb{K})$. Equation 8.6 provides an important description of the $\mathbb{R}$-inner product of vectors $X, Y \in \mathfrak{g}$:

$$(8.8) \qquad \langle X, Y \rangle_\mathbb{R} = \mathrm{Real}(\mathrm{trace}(X \cdot Y^*)).$$

Proposition 8.12 can be restated as follows:

Corollary 8.13. *If the fixed basis $\mathcal{B}$ of $\mathfrak{g}$ is orthonormal with respect to $\langle \cdot, \cdot \rangle_{\mathbb{R}}$, then $\mathrm{Ad}_g \in O(d)$ for all $g \in G$. Thus, $\mathrm{Ad} : G \to O(d)$ is a homomorphism into the orthogonal group.*

Proof. For all $g \in G$, $\mathrm{Ad}_g : \mathfrak{g} \to \mathfrak{g}$ preserves norms and therefore also inner products. That is, $\langle \mathrm{Ad}(X), \mathrm{Ad}(Y) \rangle_{\mathbb{R}} = \langle X, Y \rangle_{\mathbb{R}}$ for all $X, Y \in \mathfrak{g}$. The result now follows from Exercise 3.14.   □

An important consequence is that Lie brackets interact with the $\mathbb{R}$-inner product in the following way:

Proposition 8.14. *If G is a subgroup of $\mathcal{O}_n(\mathbb{K})$, then for all vectors $X, Y, Z \in \mathfrak{g}$,*
$$\langle [X, Y], Z \rangle_{\mathbb{R}} = -\langle [X, Z], Y \rangle_{\mathbb{R}}.$$

Proof. Let $\alpha(t)$ be a path in G with $\alpha(0) = I$ and $\alpha'(0) = X$. Since $\langle \cdot, \cdot \rangle_{\mathbb{R}}$ is Ad-invariant:
$$
\begin{aligned}
0 &= \left. \frac{d}{dt} \right|_{t=0} \langle \mathrm{Ad}_{\alpha(t)} Y, \mathrm{Ad}_{\alpha(t)} Z \rangle_{\mathbb{R}} \\
&= \left\langle \left. \frac{d}{dt} \right|_{t=0} \mathrm{Ad}_{\alpha(t)} Y, Z \right\rangle_{\mathbb{R}} + \left\langle Y, \left. \frac{d}{dt} \right|_{t=0} \mathrm{Ad}_{\alpha(t)} Z \right\rangle_{\mathbb{R}} \\
&= \langle [X, Y], Z \rangle_{\mathbb{R}} + \langle Y, [X, Z] \rangle_{\mathbb{R}}.
\end{aligned}
$$
The second equality uses the rule $\langle A, B \rangle' = \langle A', B \rangle + \langle A, B' \rangle$, which is a basic differentiation rule for the dot product found in any multi-variable calculus textbook.   □

We end this section by looking more carefully at Equation 8.7, which said that for all $g \in \mathcal{O}_n(\mathbb{K})$ and all $X \in M_n(\mathbb{K})$,
$$|Xg| = |gX| = |X|.$$

We learned back in Chapter 3 that left or right multiplication by g determined an isometry of $\mathbb{K}^n \cong \mathbb{R}^n, \mathbb{R}^{2n}$ or $\mathbb{R}^{4n}$. Now we learn that left or right multiplication by g also determines an isometry of $M_n(\mathbb{K}) \cong \mathbb{R}^{n^2}, \mathbb{R}^{2n^2}$ or $\mathbb{R}^{4n^2}$.

This observation is crucial in <u>Riemannian geometry</u>. Whenever $G \subset \mathcal{O}_n(\mathbb{K}) \subset M_n(\mathbb{K})$ is a subgroup, and $g \in G$, then the function from $M_n(\mathbb{K})$ to $M_n(\mathbb{K})$ sending $x \mapsto gx$ (or $x \mapsto xg$) is an isometry which restricts to a function $G \to G$. This restriction is called an isometry G, because the distance between a pair of points of G is the same as the distance between their images. This remains true when the "distance" between a pair of points in G is re-defined to mean the length of the shortest path in G between them. It is interesting that subgroups of $\mathcal{O}_n(\mathbb{K})$ have so many isometries; they are highly symmetric manifolds, more so than typical non-compact matrix groups.

5. Global conclusions

By definition, the Lie bracket provides information about the group operation among elements near I. What about elements far from I? In this section, we demonstrate some global conclusion about a group which can be derived from information about its Lie algebra.

Let G be a matrix group with Lie algebra $\mathfrak{g}$. A subspace $\mathfrak{h} \subset \mathfrak{g}$ is called a sub-algebra if it is closed under the Lie bracket operation; that is, $[A, B] \in \mathfrak{h}$ for all $A, B \in \mathfrak{h}$. Further, $\mathfrak{h}$ is called an ideal if $[A, B] \in \mathfrak{h}$ for all $A \in \mathfrak{h}$ and $B \in \mathfrak{g}$. Notice that the Lie algebra of any subgroup of G is a subalgebra of $\mathfrak{g}$. We will prove:

Theorem 8.15. *Let G be a path-connected matrix group, and let $H \subset G$ be a path-connected subgroup. Denote their Lie algebras as $\mathfrak{h} \subset \mathfrak{g}$. Then H is a normal subgroup of G if and only if $\mathfrak{h}$ is an ideal of $\mathfrak{g}$.*

Proof. First assume that H is a normal subgroup of G. Let $A \in \mathfrak{h}$ and $B \in \mathfrak{g}$. Let $a(t)$ be a path in H with $a(0) = I$ and $a'(0) = A$. Let $b(t)$ be a path in G with $b(0) = I$ and $b'(0) = B$.

$$[A, B] = -[B, A] = -\frac{d}{dt}\Big|_{t=0} Ad_{b(t)} A$$

$$= -\frac{d}{dt}\Big|_{t=0} \left(\frac{d}{ds}\Big|_{s=0} b(t)a(s)b(t)^{-1} \right).$$

Since H is normal in G, $b(t)a(s)b(t)^{-1} \in H$, which implies $[A, B] \in \mathfrak{h}$.

Next assume that $\mathfrak{h}$ is an ideal of $\mathfrak{g}$. For every $B \in \mathfrak{g}$ and every $A \in \mathfrak{h}$,

$$Ad_{e^B} A \in \mathfrak{h},$$

because it is the limit of a series of elements of $\mathfrak{h}$ by Theorem 8.10:

$$\mathrm{Ad}_{e^B} A = e^{\mathrm{ad}_B}(A)$$
$$= A + [B, A] + (1/2)[B, [B, A]] + (1/6)[B, [B, [B, A]]] + \cdots .$$

Now let $a \in H$ and $b \in G$. Assume that a and b lie in a small neighborhood, U, of I in G, so that $a = e^A$ for some $A \in \mathfrak{h}$ and $b = e^B$ for some $B \in \mathfrak{g}$. Then

$$bab^{-1} = be^A b^{-1} = e^{bAb^{-1}} = e^{Ad_b(A)} \in H.$$

We leave the reader (in Exercise 8.3) to show that $bab^{-1} \in H$ for all $a \in H$ and $b \in G$ (not necessarily close to I). $\qquad\square$

The previous proof demonstrates that it is possible to derive a global conclusion about a matrix group (H is normal in G) from a hypothesis about its Lie algebras ($\mathfrak{h}$ is an ideal of $\mathfrak{g}$). The Lie algebra, with its Lie bracket operation, seems to encode a lot of information about the matrix group. It turns out that the Lie bracket operation in $\mathfrak{g}$ completely determines the group operation in G, at least in a neighborhood of the identity! An explicit verification of this surprising claim is provided by the Campbell-Baker-Hausdorff series. For $X, Y, Z \in \mathfrak{g}$ with sufficiently small norm, the equation $e^X e^Y = e^Z$ has a power series solution for Z in terms of repeated Lie brackets of X and Y. The beginning of the series is:

$$Z = X + Y + (1/2)[X, Y] + (1/12)[X, [X, Y]] + (1/12)[Y, [Y, X]] + \cdots$$

The existence of such a series means that the group operation is completely determined by the Lie bracket operation; the product of e^X and e^Y can be expressed purely in term of repeated Lie brackets of X and Y.

One important consequence of the Campbell-Baker-Hausdorff series is the following correspondence between Lie algebras and matrix groups.

Theorem 8.16 (The Lie Correspondence Theorem). *There is a natural one-to-one correspondence between sub-algebras of $gl_n(\mathbb{R})$ and path-connected subgroups of $GL_n(\mathbb{R})$.*

Under this correspondence, the path-connected subgroup $H \subset GL_n(\mathbb{R})$ is mapped to its Lie algebra, $\mathfrak{g}(H) \subset gl_n(\mathbb{R})$. In the other direction, a sub-algebra $\mathfrak{h} \subset gl_n(\mathbb{R})$ is mapped to the group $\Gamma(\mathfrak{h})$ generated by the set $\{\exp(A) \mid A \in \mathfrak{h}\}$, which means the group of all finite products of elements from this set and their inverses.

Why is this a bijective correspondence? For any path-connected subgroup $H \subset GL_n(\mathbb{R})$, the fact that $\Gamma(\mathfrak{g}(H)) = H$ follows from Theorem 7.1 and Exercise 8.3, at least in the case when H is closed. The case where H is not closed requires no new arguments.

For any sub-algebra $\mathfrak{h} \subset gl_n(\mathbb{R})$, the fact that $\mathfrak{g}(\Gamma(\mathfrak{h})) = \mathfrak{h}$ is much more difficult. See [11] for a complete proof.

We conclude this section with a caution: the Lie algebra, $\mathfrak{g}$, of a matrix group, G, contains information only about the identity component G_0 of G (defined in Exercise 7.6). For example, $G = SL_n(\mathbb{Z})$ (defined in Exercise 1.8) has identity component $G_0 = \{I\}$ and Lie algebra $\mathfrak{g} = \{0\}$. This matrix group is comprised of discrete points; the Lie algebra tells you nothing about the interesting group operation on these discrete points.

6. The double cover $Sp(1) \to SO(3)$

In this section, we study the adjoint action of $Sp(1)$:

$$\text{Ad} : Sp(1) \to O(3).$$

Since $Sp(1)$ is path-connected (by Exercise 4.15), so is its image under Ad (by Exercise 4.16), so we in fact have a smooth homomorphism:

$$\text{Ad} : Sp(1) \to SO(3).$$

Our goal is to prove that $\text{Ad} : Sp(1) \to SO(3)$ is a surjective, 2-to-1 local diffeomorphism. The term "local diffeomorphism" means that there exists a neighborhood of any point of the domain, restricted to which the function is a diffeomorphism onto its image. A surjective 2-to-1 local diffeomorphism between compact manifolds is often called a double cover. This double cover provides an extremely useful tool for better understanding both $Sp(1)$ and $SO(3)$. For $g \in Sp(1)$ (regarded as a unit-length quaternion) and for $v \in sp(1) = \text{span}\{\mathbf{i}, \mathbf{j}, \mathbf{k}\}$, we have that

$$Ad_g(v) = gvg^{-1} \in sp(1).$$

Notice that conjugation by g determines an isometry $\mathbb{H} \rightarrow \mathbb{H}$, which fixes span$\{1\}$ and thus also fixes $sp(1) = $ span$\{\mathbf{i}, \mathbf{j}, \mathbf{k}\}$. So the adjoint action of $Sp(1)$ can be regarded as conjugation restricted to the purely imaginary quaternions.

Ad is a 2-to-1 map, because its kernel has two elements:

Lemma 8.17. $Ker(Ad) = \{1, -1\}$.

Proof. If $g \in \text{Ker}(\text{Ad})$, then $gvg^{-1} = v$ for all $v \in sp(1)$. In other words, g commutes with all purely imaginary quaternions, and hence with all quaternions. So $g \in \mathbb{R}$ by Exercise 1.18, which means that $g = \pm 1$. $\square$

Lemma 8.18. *Ad is a local diffeomorphism at I. In other words, Ad restricted to a sufficiently small neighborhood of I in $Sp(1)$ is a diffeomorphism onto its image.*

Proof. By the Inverse Function Theorem 7.22, it will suffice to prove that $d(\text{Ad})_I : sp(1) \rightarrow so(3)$ sends the natural basis $\{\mathbf{i}, \mathbf{j}, \mathbf{k}\}$ of $sp(1)$ to a basis of $so(3)$.

The path $\gamma(t) = e^{\mathbf{i}t} = \cos(t) + \mathbf{i}\sin(t)$ in $Sp(1)$ satisfies $\gamma(0) = I$ and $\gamma'(0) = \mathbf{i}$. For all $v \in sp(1) = $ span$\{\mathbf{i}, \mathbf{j}, \mathbf{k}\}$,

$$\frac{d}{dt}\Big|_{t=0} \text{Ad}_{\gamma(t)}(v) = \frac{d}{dt}\Big|_{t=0} e^{\mathbf{i}t}ve^{-\mathbf{i}t} = \mathbf{i}v - v\mathbf{i} = \begin{cases} 0 \text{ if } v = \mathbf{i} \\ 2\mathbf{k} \text{ if } v = \mathbf{j} \\ -2\mathbf{j} \text{ if } v = \mathbf{k} \end{cases}.$$

This shows that

$$d(\text{Ad})_I(\mathbf{i}) = \begin{pmatrix} 0 & 0 & 0 \\ 0 & 0 & -2 \\ 0 & 2 & 0 \end{pmatrix}.$$

Now repeat this argument with $\mathbf{j}$ and $\mathbf{k}$ to verify that

$$\{d(\text{Ad})_I(\mathbf{i}), d(\text{Ad})_I(\mathbf{j}), d(\text{Ad})_I(\mathbf{k})\}$$

is a basis of $so(3)$. $\square$

It follows from Exercise 8.2 at the end of this chapter that Ad is a local diffeomorphism at every $g \in Sp(1)$ (not just at the identity).

We prove next that every element of $SO(3)$ is in the image of Ad. This might be surprising, since elements in the image are all Lie algebra isomorphisms of $sp(1)$. But this restriction is redundant, since matrices in $SO(3)$ preserve the vector cross-product in $\mathbb{R}^3$, which is the same as the Lie bracket operation in $sp(1)$, and are therefore automatically Lie algebra isomorphisms.

Lemma 8.19. $Ad: Sp(1) \to SO(3)$ *is surjective.*

Proof. Since $Sp(1)$ is compact (by Exercise 4.15), its image under Ad is compact (by Proposition 4.25) and therefore closed. On the other hand, this image is open by the local diffeomorphism property. Thus, the image is a non-empty clopen subset of $SO(3)$. Since $SO(3)$ is path-connected (by Exercise 4.14), its only non-empty clopen subset is all of $SO(3)$ (see Proposition 4.18). $\qquad\qquad\square$

This double cover $Sp(1) \to SO(3)$ has many implications. It explains why $Sp(1)$ and $SO(3)$ have isomorphic Lie algebras. Its algebraic import can be summarized as follows:

$$SO(3) \text{ is isomorphic to } Sp(1)/\{I, -I\},$$

which makes sense because $\{I, -I\}$ is a normal subgroup of $Sp(1)$.

Its geometric import has to do with the shape of $SO(3)$. We will show that $SO(3)$ is diffeomorphic to an important manifold called $\mathbb{RP}^3$.

Definition 8.20. *The set of all lines through the origin in $\mathbb{R}^{n+1}$ is called n-dimensional real projective space and is denoted as $\mathbb{RP}^n$.*

Since every line through the origin in $\mathbb{R}^{n+1}$ intersects the sphere S^n in a pair of antipodal points, one often identifies $\mathbb{RP}^n$ with the set of antipodal pairs on S^n. The identification $SO(3) \cong Sp(1)/\{I, -I\}$ associates each point of $SO(3)$ with a pair of antipodal points on the sphere $S^3 \cong Sp(1)$, and therefore provides a bijection between $SO(3)$ and $\mathbb{RP}^3$. This natural bijection helps us understand the shape of $SO(3)$.

It may seem inappropriate that we referred to $\mathbb{RP}^n$ as a manifold, since it is not a subset of any Euclidean space. There is a more general definition of "manifold" under which $\mathbb{RP}^n$ can be proven to be one. For our purposes, it suffices to regard $\mathbb{RP}^3$ as a manifold by identifying it with $SO(3)$, which we know is a manifold.

We learned in Exercise 7.13 that $SO(3)$ is diffeomorphic to $T^1 S^2$, which is another way to visualize the shape of $SO(3)$. In topology, one uses an invariant called "fundamental groups" to prove the following:

Proposition 8.21. *No pair of the following three 3-dimensional manifolds is homeomorphic:*

(1) $T^1 S^2 = SO(3) = \mathbb{RP}^3$,

(2) $S^3 = Sp(1) = SU(2)$,

(3) $S^2 \times S^1$.

In particular, $SO(3)$ is not homeomorphic to $S^2 \times S^1$, which implies a negative answer to Question 1.2 from Chapter 1. Airline engineers have an intuitive appreciation for the fact that $T^1 S^2$ is different from $S^2 \times S^1$. Because of this difference, it is impossible to construct a continuously changing basis for all of the tangent spaces of S^2. For example, the "east and north" basis does not extend continuously over the north and south poles of a globe. This phenomenon underlies the subtlety of describing travel on the surface of the Earth. It also underlies the complexity of the shape of $SO(3)$.

The double cover Ad : $Sp(1) \to SO(3)$ can be used to construct important finite groups. If $H \subset SO(3)$ is a finite subgroup (these are classified in Section 3.7), then

$$\mathrm{Ad}^{-1}(H) := \{q \in Sp(1) \mid \mathrm{Ad}_q \in H\}$$

is a finite subgroup of $Sp(1)$ with twice the order of H. For example let $H \subset SO(3)$ denote the direct symmetry group of the icosahedron, which is isomorphic to A_5 (see Section 3.7). Let $H^* := \mathrm{Ad}^{-1}(H) \subset Sp(1)$. H has order 60 and is called the *icosahedral group*. H^* has order 120 and is called the *binary icosahedral group*. The set of cosets $Sp(1)/H^*$ is a three-dimensional manifold called the *Poincaré dodecahedral space*. This manifold is very recently of great interest to cosmologists because it has been proposed as a good candidate for the shape of the universe [14].

7. Other double covers

It turns out that for every $n > 2$, there is a matrix group which double-covers $SO(n)$. The first few are:

$$Sp(1) \to SO(3)$$
$$Sp(1) \times Sp(1) \to SO(4)$$
$$Sp(2) \to SO(5)$$
$$SU(4) \to SO(6)$$

In general, the double cover of $SO(n)$ is denoted $\mathrm{Spin}(n)$ and is called the spin group, not to be confused with the symplectic group, $Sp(n)$. For $3 \leq n \leq 6$, $\mathrm{Spin}(n)$ is as above. For $n > 6$, $\mathrm{Spin}(n)$ is not isomorphic to any thus far familiar matrix groups. See [3] for a construction of the spin groups.

Since these double covers are group homomorphisms, the Lie algebra of $\mathrm{Spin}(n)$ is isomorphic to the Lie algebra of $SO(n)$. Thus,

$$sp(1) \cong so(3)$$
$$sp(1) \times sp(1) \cong so(4)$$
$$sp(2) \cong so(5)$$
$$su(4) \cong so(6)$$

We will describe only the second double cover above, denoted

$$F : Sp(1) \times Sp(1) \to SO(4).$$

Remember that $Sp(1) \times Sp(1)$ is a matrix group by Exercise 1.10. The double cover is defined such that for $(g_1, g_2) \in Sp(1) \times Sp(1)$ and $v \in \mathbb{R}^4 \cong \mathbb{H}$,

$$F(g_1, g_2)(v) = g_1 v \bar{g}_2.$$

By arguments completely analogous to the previous section, the image of F is $SO(4)$, and F is a smooth 2-to-1 homomorphism and a local diffeomorphism at every point. The kernel of F is $\{(I, I), (-I, -I)\}$, which means that:

$$SO(4) \cong (Sp(1) \times Sp(1)) / \{(I, I), (-I, -I)\}$$

The derivative $dF_{(I,I)} : sp(1) \times sp(1) \to so(4)$ is the following Lie algebra isomorphism:

$$dF_{(I,I)}(a\mathbf{i}+b\mathbf{j}+c\mathbf{k}, x\mathbf{i}+y\mathbf{j}+z\mathbf{k}) = \begin{pmatrix} 0 & -a-x & -b-y & -c-z \\ a+x & 0 & -c+z & b-y \\ b+y & c-z & 0 & -a+x \\ c+z & -b+y & a-x & 0 \end{pmatrix}$$

This is straightforward to verify on basis elements. For example,

$$\frac{d}{dt}\bigg|_{t=0} F(e^{\mathbf{i}t}, 1)(v) = \frac{d}{dt}\bigg|_{t=0} e^{\mathbf{i}t}v = \mathbf{i}v = \begin{cases} \mathbf{i} \text{ if } v = 1 \\ -1 \text{ if } v = \mathbf{i} \\ \mathbf{k} \text{ if } v = \mathbf{j} \\ -\mathbf{j} \text{ if } v = \mathbf{k} \end{cases}$$

which shows that

$$dF_{(I,I)}(\mathbf{i}, 0) = \begin{pmatrix} 0 & -1 & 0 & 0 \\ 1 & 0 & 0 & 0 \\ 0 & 0 & 0 & -1 \\ 0 & 0 & 1 & 0 \end{pmatrix}.$$

The vectors $(\mathbf{j}, 0), (\mathbf{k}, 0), (0, \mathbf{i}), (0, \mathbf{j})$ and $(0, \mathbf{k})$ are handled similarly.

The fact that $so(4)$ is isomorphic to $sp(1) \times sp(1)$ has many important consequences. It is the essential starting point on which the inter-related theories of 4-dimensional manifolds, Yang-Mills connections, and particle physics are built.

8. Exercises

Ex. 8.1. Question 1.1 in Chapter 1 asked whether $SO(3)$ is an abelian group. Prove that it is not in two ways: first by finding two elements of $so(3)$ which do not commute, and second by finding two elements of $SO(3)$ which do not commute. Which is easier? Prove that $SO(n)$ is not abelian for any $n > 2$.

Ex. 8.2. Let G_1, G_2 be matrix groups with Lie algebras $\mathfrak{g}_1, \mathfrak{g}_2$. Suppose that $f : G_1 \to G_2$ is a smooth homomorphism. If $df_I : \mathfrak{g}_1 \to \mathfrak{g}_2$ is bijective, prove that $df_g : T_g G_1 \to T_{f(g)} G_2$ is bijective for all $g \in G_1$.

Ex. 8.3.

(1) Let G be a path-connected matrix group, and let U be a neighborhood of I in G. Prove that U generates G, which means that every element of G is equal to a finite product $g_1 g_2 \cdots g_k$, where for each i, g_i or g_i^{-1} lies in U.

(2) In the proof of Theorem 8.15, remove the restriction that a and b are close to the identity.

Ex. 8.4. Define $d : Sp(1) \to Sp(1) \times Sp(1)$ as $a \mapsto (a, a)$. Explicitly describe the function $\iota : SO(3) \to SO(4)$ for which the following diagram commutes:

$$
\begin{array}{ccc}
Sp(1) & \xrightarrow{\ d\ } & Sp(1) \times Sp(1) \\
\scriptstyle\text{Ad}\big\downarrow & & \big\downarrow\scriptstyle F \\
SO(3) & \xrightarrow{\ \iota\ } & SO(4)
\end{array}
$$

Ex. 8.5. Express $so(4)$ as the direct sum of two 3-dimensional subspaces, each of which is an ideal of $so(4)$. Show there is a unique way to do so.

Ex. 8.6. Prove that $Sp(1) \times SO(3)$ is not smoothly isomorphic to $SO(4)$. *Hint: A smooth isomorphism would be determined by its derivative at (I, I), which would send ideals to ideals.*

Ex. 8.7. Construct an explicit diffeomorphism between $SO(4)$ and $Sp(1) \times SO(3)$.

Ex. 8.8. Does there exist a basis for $u(2)$ such that the function $\text{Ad} : U(2) \to O(4)$ is the familiar injective map, denoted as ρ_2 in Chapter 2?

Ex. 8.9. Let G be a path-connected matrix group, and let $H \subset G$ be a path-connected subgroup. Denote their Lie algebras as $\mathfrak{h} \subset \mathfrak{g}$. H is called <u>central</u> if $gh = hg$ for all $g \in G$ and $h \in H$. Prove that H is central if and only if $[X, Y] = 0$ for all $X \in \mathfrak{g}$ and $Y \in \mathfrak{h}$.

Ex. 8.10. Do $SO(3)$ and $\text{Isom}(\mathbb{R}^2)$ have isomorphic Lie algebras?

Ex. 8.11. For a matrix group G of dimension d, prove that the function $\text{Ad} : G \to GL_d(\mathbb{R})$ is smooth.

Ex. 8.12. Let G be a matrix group with Lie algebra $\mathfrak{g}$ and $A_1, A_2 \in \mathfrak{g}$.

(1) Prove that the path

$$\gamma(t) = e^{tA_1} e^{tA_2} e^{-tA_1} e^{-tA_2}$$

satisfies $\gamma(0) = I$, $\gamma'(t) = 0$ and $\gamma''(0) = 2[A_1, A_2]$. This is another precise sense in which $[A_1, A_2]$ measures the failure of e^{tA_1} and e^{tA_2} to commute for small t.

(2) Explicitly verify this when $\{A_1, A_2\}$ is a natural basis for the Lie algebra of $\text{Aff}_1(\mathbb{R})$. Explain visually in terms of translations and scalings of $\mathbb{R}$.

(3) Use a computer algebra system to explicitly verify this when $G = SO(3)$, and A_1, A_2 are the first two elements of the basis of $so(3)$ in Equation 8.2. In this example, is $\gamma(t)$ a one-parameter group? Explain this result in terms of rotations of a globe.

Ex. 8.13. Let G be a closed subgroup of $O(n)$, $U(n)$ or $Sp(n)$. Let $\mathfrak{g}$ be the Lie algebra of G. Let $\mathfrak{h} \subset \mathfrak{g}$ be a subalgebra, and denote

$$\mathfrak{h}^{\perp} := \{A \in \mathfrak{g} \mid \langle X, A \rangle = 0 \text{ for all } X \in \mathfrak{h}\}.$$

(1) If $X \in \mathfrak{h}$ and $A \in \mathfrak{h}^{\perp}$, prove that $[X, A] \in \mathfrak{h}^{\perp}$.

(2) If $\mathfrak{h}$ is an ideal, prove that $\mathfrak{h}^{\perp}$ is also an ideal.

Ex. 8.14. In contrast to the fact that $T^1 S^2 \neq S^2 \times S^1$, prove that $T^1 S^3$ is diffeomorphic to $S^3 \times S^2$, and more generally that $T^1 G$ is diffeomorphic to $G \times S^{d-1}$ for any matrix group G of dimension d.

Chapter 9

Maximal tori

In Chapter 1, we regarded $SO(3)$ as the group of positions of a globe. We asked whether every element of $SO(3)$ can be achieved, starting at the identity position, by rotating through some angle about some single axis. In other words, is every element of $SO(3)$ just a rotation? In this chapter, we provide an affirmative answer. Much more generally, we characterize elements of $SO(n)$, $SU(n)$, $U(n)$ and $Sp(n)$. An elements of any of these groups is just a simultaneous rotation in a collection of orthogonal planes.

To explain and prove this characterization, we must understand *maximal tori*, a fundamental tool for studying compact matrix groups. We use maximal tori in this chapter to prove several important theorems about familiar compact matrix groups, including:

Theorem 9.1. *Let* $G \in \{SO(n), U(n), SU(n), Sp(n)\}$.

(1) *Every element of* G *equals* e^X *for some* X *in the Lie algebra of* G.

(2) G *is path-connected.*

Notice that part (2) follows from part (1), since every element of G is connected to the identity by a one-parameter group. It turns out that part (1) is true when G is any compact path-connected matrix group, but is false for several path-connected non-compact matrix groups, like $SL_2(\mathbb{R})$ and $SL_2(\mathbb{C})$.

To understand the group operation in a matrix group, G, you must understand which elements commute with which elements. If G is compact and path-connected, maximal tori provide a clean way to explicitly describe, for each $x \in G$, the set of elements of G which commute with x. They also help us determine the <u>center</u>, $Z(G)$, defined as:

$$Z(G) := \{g \in G \mid ga = ag \text{ for all } a \in G\}.$$

For example, we will prove that $SO(3)$ and $SU(2)$ are not isomorphic by showing that their centers are not isomorphic. The size of $Z(G)$ measures how much commuting there is in G. We will see that the size (dimension) of a maximal torus of G also measures the amount of commuting in G.

1. Several characterizations of a torus

In this section, we define a torus and prove that tori are the only path-connected compact abelian matrix groups.

Remember that $U(1) = \{(e^{i\theta}) \mid \theta \in [0, 2\pi)\}$ is the circle-group whose group operation is addition of angles. $U(1)$ is abelian, path-connected, and isomorphic to $SO(2)$.

Definition 9.2. *The n-dimensional <u>torus</u> T^n is the group*

$$T^n := U(1) \times U(1) \times \cdots \times U(1) \text{ (n copies).}$$

In general, the product of two or more matrix groups is isomorphic to a matrix group by Exercise 1.10. In this case,

$$T^n \cong \{\text{diag}(e^{i\theta_1}, ..., e^{i\theta_n}) \mid \theta_i \in [0, 2\pi)\} \subset GL_n(\mathbb{C}).$$

There is a useful alternative description of T^n. Remember $(\mathbb{R}^n, +)$ denotes the group of vectors in Euclidean space under the operation of vector addition. $(\mathbb{R}^n, +)$ is isomorphic to a matrix group, namely $\text{Trans}(\mathbb{R}^n)$, as explained in Section 6 of Chapter 3.

In group theory, if $a_1, ..., a_k$ are elements of a group, G, one often denotes the subgroup of G which they generate as $\langle a_1, ..., a_k \rangle \subset G$. This means the group of all finite products of the a's and their inverses. For example, if $\{v_1, ..., v_k\} \subset (\mathbb{R}^n, +)$, then

$$\langle v_1, ..., v_k \rangle = \{n_1 v_1 + \cdots + n_k v_k \mid n_i \in \mathbb{Z}\},$$

where $\mathbb{Z} = \{..., -2, -1, 0, 1, 2, ...\}$ denotes the integers. Since $(\mathbb{R}^n, +)$ is an abelian group, any subgroup $N \subset (\mathbb{R}^n, +)$ is normal, so the coset space $(\mathbb{R}^n, +)/N$ is a group.

Proposition 9.3. *If* $\{v_1, ..., v_n\} \subset \mathbb{R}^n$ *is a basis, then the quotient group* $(\mathbb{R}^n, +)/\langle v_1, ..., v_n \rangle$ *is isomorphic to* T^n.

Proof. We first prove the proposition for the standard basis of $\mathbb{R}^n$,

$$\{e_1 = (1, 0, ..., 0), e_2 = (0, 1, 0, ..., 0), ..., e_n = (0, ..., 0, 1)\}.$$

The homomorphism $f : (\mathbb{R}^n, +) \to T^n$ defined as

$$f(t_1, ..., t_n) := \mathrm{diag}(e^{2\pi i t_1}, ..., e^{2\pi i t_n})$$

is surjective. The kernel of f equals $\langle e_1, ..., e_n \rangle$. Therefore, T^n is isomorphic to $(\mathbb{R}^n, +)/\langle e_1, ..., e_n \rangle$.

Next let $\{v_1, ..., v_n\}$ be any basis of $\mathbb{R}^n$. Let $A \in GL_n(\mathbb{R})$ have rows equal to $v_1, ..., v_n$, so that $R_A(e_i) = v_i$ for all $i = 1, ..., n$. The function $R_A : (\mathbb{R}^n, +) \to (\mathbb{R}^n, +)$ is an isomorphism, which sends the subgroup generated by the e's to the subgroup generated by the v's. It follows that

$$(\mathbb{R}^n, +)/\langle v_1, ..., v_n \rangle \cong (\mathbb{R}^n, +)/\langle e_1, ..., e_n \rangle \cong T^n.$$

$\square$

Corollary 9.4. *If* $\{v_1, ..., v_k\} \subset \mathbb{R}^n$ *is a linearly independent set, then* $(\mathbb{R}^n, +)/\langle v_1, ..., v_k \rangle$ *is isomorphic to* $T^k \times (\mathbb{R}^{n-k}, +)$.

Proof. Choosing vectors $v_{k+1}, ..., v_n$ so that the v's form a basis of $\mathbb{R}^n$,

$$(\mathbb{R}^n, +)/\langle v_1, ..., v_k \rangle$$
$$\cong ((\mathrm{span}\{v_1, ..., v_k\}, +)/\langle v_1, ..., v_k \rangle) \times (\mathrm{span}\{v_{k+1}, ..., v_n\}, +)$$
$$\cong T^k \times (\mathbb{R}^{n-k}, +).$$

$\square$

The term "torus" is justified by an important way to visualize T^2. Figure 1 shows the subgroup $\langle v_1, v_2 \rangle \subset \mathbb{R}^2$ generated by a basis $\{v_1, v_2\}$ of $\mathbb{R}^2$. The coset of $\mathbb{R}^2/\langle v_1, v_2 \rangle$ containing a typical vector $w \in \mathbb{R}^2$ is pictured as a collection of grey circles. For most choices of $w \in \mathbb{R}^2$, this coset will intersect a <u>fundamental domain</u> (like the pictured parallelogram) in exactly one point. However, there are some exceptions. If $w \in \langle v_1, v_2 \rangle$, then the coset intersects the fundamental domain in its four corners. If $w = nv_1 + tv_2$ for some $n \in \mathbb{Z}$ and some $t \in \mathbb{R}$ ($t \notin \mathbb{Z}$), then the coset intersects the fundamental domain in two points, one on its top and one on its bottom edge. Similarly, if $w = tv_1 + nv_2$, then the coset intersects the left and right edge of the fundamental domain.

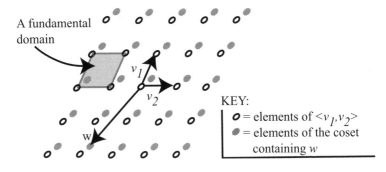

Figure 1. A coset of $\mathbb{R}^2 / \langle v_1, v_2 \rangle$.

So T^n can be identified with the fundamental domain, with the understanding that a point w on its left edge is considered the same as the point $w + v_2$ on its right edge, and a point w on its bottom edge is considered the same as a point $w + v_1$ on its top edge. If you cut a parallelogram out of paper and glue its left edge to its right edge, you obtain a cylinder. If you then glue the top edge to the bottom edge, you obtain the donut-shaped object commonly referred to as a torus; see the torus of revolution illustration in Section 7.4.

It is easy to see that T^n is compact, abelian and path-connected. We end this section by proving that these properties characterize tori.

Theorem 9.5. *Any compact, abelian path-connected matrix group, G, is isomorphic to a torus.*

Proof. Let $\mathfrak{g}$ denote the Lie algebra of G. Since G is abelian, we have $AB = BA$, and therefore $e^A e^B = e^{A+B}$ for all $A, B \in \mathfrak{g}$. This equality means that the exponential map $\exp : \mathfrak{g} \to G$ is a group homomorphism, when $\mathfrak{g}$ is considered as a group under vector addition.

Let $K \subset \mathfrak{g}$ denote the kernel of $\exp$. K is a <u>discrete</u> subgroup of $\mathfrak{g}$, which means that there exists a neighborhood, U, of the origin (= the identity) in $\mathfrak{g}$ whose intersection with K contains only the origin, namely, any neighborhood on which $\exp$ is a diffeomorphism. It follows that any vector $v \in K$ has a neighborhood in $\mathfrak{g}$ separating it from all other elements of K; namely, $v + U := \{v + u \mid u \in U\}$.

Since K is discrete, we claim that $K = \langle v_1, .., v_k \rangle$ for some linearly independent set $\{v_1, ..., v_k\} \subset \mathfrak{g}$, with $k \leq \dim(\mathfrak{g})$. For clarity, we will only indicate the argument when $\dim(\mathfrak{g}) = 2$, although the idea generalizes to any dimension.

Let $v_1 \in K$ denote a non-zero vector of minimal norm. Such a vector exists because K is discrete. If $\langle v_1 \rangle = K$, then the claim is true with $k = 1$. Otherwise, let v_2 denote a vector of minimal norm among candidates in K but not in $\langle v_1 \rangle$. Since K is a subgroup, $\langle v_1, v_2 \rangle \subset K$. We claim that $\langle v_1, v_2 \rangle = K$. Suppose to the contrary that some vector $w \in K$ is not contained in $\langle v_1, v_2 \rangle$. Then the four grey vectors pictured in Figure 2 are contained in K. It is straightforward to check that at least one of the four is too short, meaning it contradicts the minimal-norm property of v_1 or v_2.

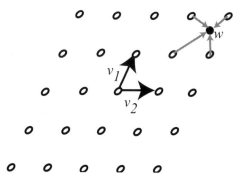

Figure 2. Proof that $\langle v_2, v_2 \rangle = K$.

Next we claim that $\exp : \mathfrak{g} \to G$ is surjective. The image, $\exp(\mathfrak{g}) \subset G$, contains a neighborhood, V, of the identity in G. Since $\exp(\mathfrak{g})$ is a subgroup of G, it contains the set $\langle V \rangle$ consisting of all products of finitely many elements of V and their inverses. We prove now that $\langle V \rangle = G$ (which amounts to proving part (1) of Exercise 8.3). Since G is path-connected, it will suffice by Proposition 4.18 to prove that $\langle V \rangle$ is clopen in G. First, $\langle V \rangle$ is open in G because for any $g \in \langle V \rangle$, the set $g \cdot V := \{ga \mid a \in V\}$ is a neighborhood of g in G which is contained in $\langle V \rangle$. Second, to prove that $\langle V \rangle$ is closed in G, let $g \in G$ be a limit point of $\langle V \rangle$. The neighborhood $g \cdot V$ of g in G must contain some $b \in \langle V \rangle$; that is, $ga = b$ for some $a, b \in \langle V \rangle$. So $g = ba^{-1}$ is a product of two elements of $\langle V \rangle$, which shows that $g \in \langle V \rangle$.

In summary, $\exp : \mathfrak{g} \to G$ is a surjective homomorphism whose kernel equals $\langle v_1, ..., v_k \rangle$. So,

$$G \cong \mathfrak{g}/\langle v_1, ..., v_k \rangle \cong T^k \times (\mathbb{R}^{d-k}, +),$$

where $d = \dim(\mathfrak{g})$. Since G is compact, we must have $d = k$. $\qquad \square$

The above proof actually verifies the following more general theorem:

Theorem 9.6. *Any abelian path-connected matrix group is isomorphic to $T^k \times (\mathbb{R}^m, +)$ for some integers $k, m \geq 0$.*

2. The standard maximal torus and center of $SO(n)$, $SU(n)$, $U(n)$ and $Sp(n)$

Definition 9.7. *Let G be a matrix group. A* torus in G *means a subgroup of G which is isomorphic to a torus. A* maximal torus in G *means a torus in G which is not contained in a higher dimensional torus in G.*

Every matrix group G contains at least one maximal torus, which is justified as follows. The subgroup $\{I\} \subset G$ is a 0-dimensional torus in G. If it is not contained in a 1-dimensional torus, then it is maximal. Otherwise, choose a 1-dimensional torus T^1 in G. If T^1 is not contained in a 2-dimensional torus, then it is maximal.

Otherwise, choose a 2-dimensional torus T^2 in G containing T^1, etc. This process must stop, since G clearly can not contain a torus with dimension higher than its own.

Maximal tori are really useful only for studying path-connected compact matrix groups. So, in this section, we will determine maximal tori of our familiar compact matrix groups: $SO(n)$, $U(n)$, $SU(n)$ and $Sp(n)$.

We will use "diag" as a shorthand for <u>block-diagonal</u> matrices as well as diagonal matrices. For example,

$$\text{diag}\left(\begin{pmatrix} 1 & 2 \\ 3 & 4 \end{pmatrix}, \begin{pmatrix} 5 & 6 & 7 \\ 8 & 9 & 10 \\ 11 & 12 & 13 \end{pmatrix}, 14 \right) := \begin{pmatrix} 1 & 2 & 0 & 0 & 0 & 0 \\ 3 & 4 & 0 & 0 & 0 & 0 \\ 0 & 0 & 5 & 6 & 7 & 0 \\ 0 & 0 & 8 & 9 & 10 & 0 \\ 0 & 0 & 11 & 12 & 13 & 0 \\ 0 & 0 & 0 & 0 & 0 & 14 \end{pmatrix}.$$

Notice that the product of similarly shaped block-diagonal matrices is calculated blockwise. For example, when $A_1, B_1 \in M_{n_1}(\mathbb{K})$ and when $A_2, B_2 \in M_{n_2}(\mathbb{K})$, we have:

$$\text{diag}(A_1, A_2) \cdot \text{diag}(B_1, B_2) = \text{diag}(A_1 \cdot B_1, A_2 \cdot B_2) \in M_{n_1+n_2}(\mathbb{K}).$$

Therefore, if $G_1 \subset GL_{n_1}(\mathbb{K})$ and $G_2 \subset GL_{n_2}(\mathbb{K})$ are both matrix groups, then their product $G_1 \times G_2$ is isomorphic to the following matrix group:

$$G_1 \times G_2 \cong \{\text{diag}(A_1, A_2) \mid A_1 \in G_1, A_2 \in G_2\} \subset GL_{n_1+n_2}(\mathbb{K}).$$

Also notice that the determinant of a block-diagonal matrix is the product of the determinants of its blocks.

We also introduce notation for the familiar 2-by-2 rotation matrix:

$$\mathcal{R}_\theta := \begin{pmatrix} \cos\theta & \sin\theta \\ -\sin\theta & \cos\theta \end{pmatrix}.$$

Theorem 9.8. *Each of the following is a maximal torus.*

$$T = \{diag(\mathcal{R}_{\theta_1}, ..., \mathcal{R}_{\theta_m}) \mid \theta_i \in [0, 2\pi)\} \subset SO(2m).$$

$$T = \{diag(\mathcal{R}_{\theta_1}, ..., \mathcal{R}_{\theta_m}, 1) \mid \theta_i \in [0, 2\pi)\} \subset SO(2m+1).$$

$$T = \{diag(e^{i\theta_1}, ..., e^{i\theta_n}) \mid \theta_i \in [0, 2\pi)\} \subset U(n).$$

$$T = \{diag(e^{i\theta_1}, ..., e^{i\theta_n}) \mid \theta_i \in [0, 2\pi)\} \subset Sp(n).$$

$$T = \{diag(e^{i\theta_1}, ..., e^{i\theta_{n-1}}, e^{-i(\theta_1 + \cdots + \theta_{n-1})}) \mid \theta_i \in [0, 2\pi)\} \subset SU(n).$$

In each case, the given torus T is called the <u>standard maximal torus</u> of the matrix group. It is not the only maximal torus, as we will see, but it is the simplest to describe. Notice that the standard maximal torus of $SU(n)$ is the intersection with $SU(n)$ of the standard maximal torus of $U(n)$.

Proof. In each case, it is easy to see that T is a torus. The challenge is to prove that T is not contained in a higher-dimensional torus of the group G. In each case, we will justify this by proving that any element $g \in G$ which commutes with all elements of T must lie in T. Since any element of an alleged higher-dimensional torus would commute with all elements of T, this shows that no such higher-dimensional torus could exist.

CASE 1: $SO(n)$. For clarity, we will prove that

$$T = \{diag(\mathcal{R}_{\theta_1}, \mathcal{R}_{\theta_2}, 1) \mid \theta_1, \theta_2 \in [0, 2\pi)\}$$

is a maximal torus of $SO(5)$. Our arguments will generalize in an obvious way to $SO(n)$ for all even or odd n.

Suppose that $g \in SO(5)$ commutes with every element of T. Let θ be an angle which is not an integer multiple of π. We will use that g commutes with $A := diag(\mathcal{R}_\theta, \mathcal{R}_\theta, 1) \in T$. Notice that multiples of $e_5 = (0, 0, 0, 0, 1)$ are the only vectors in $\mathbb{R}^5$ that are fixed by R_A. Since $e_5 gA = e_5 Ag = e_5 g$, we learn that R_A fixes $e_5 g$, which means $e_5 g = \pm e_5$. That is, the 5th row of g looks like $(0, 0, 0, 0, \pm 1)$.

Next, use that g commutes with $A := diag(\mathcal{R}_\theta, 1, 1, 1) \in T$. The only vectors in $\mathbb{R}^5$ fixed by R_A are in span$\{e_3, e_4, e_5\}$. For each of $i \in \{3, 4\}$, we have that $e_i gA = e_i Ag = e_i g$, so R_A fixes $e_i g$, which means that $e_i g \in$ span$\{e_3, e_4, e_5\}$. In fact, $e_i g \in$ span$\{e_3, e_4\}$, since otherwise $\langle e_i g, e_5 g \rangle \neq 0$. So the 3rd and 4th row of g each has the form $(0, 0, a, b, 0)$. Repeating this argument with $A := \text{diag}(1, 1, \mathcal{R}_\theta, 1)$ gives that the first and second row of g each has the form $(a, b, 0, 0, 0)$.

In summary, g has the form $g = \text{diag}(g_1, g_2, \pm 1)$ for some elements $g_1, g_2 \in M_2(\mathbb{R})$. Since $g \in SO(5)$, we have $g_1, g_2 \in O(2)$. It remains to prove that $g_1, g_2 \in SO(2)$, which forces the last argument to be $+1$ rather than -1 because $\det(g) = 1$. Suppose to the contrary that $g_1 \in O(2) - SO(2)$. Then g does not commute with $\text{diag}(\mathcal{R}_\theta, 1, 1, 1)$. This is because g_1 does not commute with $\mathcal{R}_\theta$ by Exercise 3.6, which states that flips of $\mathbb{R}^2$ never commute with rotations of $\mathbb{R}^2$. Therefore $g_1 \in SO(2)$, and similarly $g_2 \in SO(2)$. Therefore, $g \in T$.

<u>CASE 2: $U(n)$.</u> We will prove that
$$T := \{\text{diag}(e^{i\theta_1}, ..., e^{i\theta_n}) \mid \theta_i \in [0, 2\pi)\}$$
is a maximal torus of $U(n)$. Suppose that $g \in U(n)$ commutes with every element of T. Let θ be an angle which is not an integer multiple of π. We use that g commutes with $A := \text{diag}(e^{i\theta}, e^{i\theta}, ..., e^{i\theta}, 1) \in T$. Notice that complex multiples of $e_n = (0, ..., 0, 1)$ are the only vectors in $\mathbb{C}^n$ fixed by R_A. Since $e_n g A = e_n A g = e_n g$, we learn that R_A fixes $e_n g$, which means $e_n g = \lambda e_n$ for some $\lambda \in \mathbb{C}$. That is, the nth row of g looks like $(0, ..., 0, \lambda)$. Repeating this argument with the "1" entry of A moved to other positions gives that g is diagonal. It follows that $g \in T$.

<u>CASE 3: $Sp(n)$.</u> Suppose $g \in Sp(n)$ commutes with every element of $T := \{\text{diag}(e^{i\theta_1}, ..., e^{i\theta_n}) \mid \theta_i \in [0, 2\pi)\}$. The argument in case 2 gives that g is diagonal; that is, $g = \text{diag}(q_1, ..., q_n)$ for some $q_i \in \mathbb{H}$. Since g commutes with $\text{diag}(i, 1, ..., 1) \in T$, we know that $q_1 i = i q_1$. By Exercise 1.15, this implies that $q_1 \in \mathbb{C}$. Similarly, $q_i \in \mathbb{C}$ for $i = 1, ..., n$. It follows that $g \in T$.

<u>CASE 4: $SU(n)$.</u> For clarity, we will prove that
$$T = \{\text{diag}(e^{i\theta_1}, e^{i\theta_2}, e^{-i(\theta_1 + \theta_2)}) \mid \theta_1, \theta_2 \in [0, 2\pi)\}$$
is a maximal torus of $SU(3)$. Suppose that $g \in SU(3)$ commutes with every element of T. Since g commutes with $A = \text{diag}(1, e^{i\theta}, e^{-i\theta}) \in T$, the first row of g must be a multiple of e_1. Permuting the three

diagonal entries of A gives that the second row of g is a multiple of e_2 and the third of e_3. So g is diagonal, which implies that $g \in T$.

This argument generalizes to $SU(n)$ for all $n \geq 3$. It remains to prove that $T := \{\text{diag}(e^{i\theta}, e^{-i\theta}) \mid \theta \in [0, 2\pi)\}$ is a maximal torus of $SU(2)$. The isomorphism from $Sp(1)$ to $SU(2)$ (Section 4 of Chapter 3) sends the standard maximal torus of $Sp(1)$ to T, so this follows from case 3. $\qquad \square$

In each case of the previous proof, we verified the maximality of the standard torus by proving something slightly stronger:

Proposition 9.9. *Let $G \in \{SO(n), U(n), SU(n), Sp(n)\}$, and let T be the standard maximal torus of G. Then any element of G which commutes with every element of T must lie in T. In particular, T is maximal abelian, which means that T is not contained in any larger abelian subgroup of G.*

As an application, we will calculate the centers of $SO(n)$, $U(n)$, $Sp(n)$ and $SU(n)$. Remember that the center of a group G is defined as

$$Z(G) := \{g \in G \mid ga = ag \text{ for all } a \in G\}.$$

Theorem 9.10.

(1) $Z(SO(2m)) = \{I, -I\}$ *(the group of order 2)*.

(2) $Z(SO(2m+1)) = \{I\}$ *(the trivial group)*.

(3) $Z(U(n)) = \{e^{i\theta} \cdot I \mid \theta \in [0, 2\pi)\}$ *(isomorphic to $U(1)$)*.

(4) $Z(Sp(n)) = \{I, -I\}$.

(5) $Z(SU(n)) = \{\omega \cdot I \mid \omega^n = 1\}$ *(the cyclic group of order n)*.

Notice that $Z(SU(n)) = Z(U(n)) \cap SU(n)$.

Proof. By Proposition 9.9, the center of each of these groups is a subset of its standard maximal torus. From this starting point, the arguments are straightforward, so we will leave to the reader all but the case $G = U(n)$.

Suppose that $g \in Z(U(n))$. Since g lies in the standard maximal torus, it must be diagonal: $g = \text{diag}(\lambda_1, ..., \lambda_n)$. We will use that g

commutes with $A := \mathrm{diag}\left(\begin{pmatrix} 0 & 1 \\ 1 & 0 \end{pmatrix}, 1, ..., 1 \right) \in U(n)$:

$$\mathrm{diag}\left(\begin{pmatrix} 0 & \lambda_1 \\ \lambda_2 & 0 \end{pmatrix}, \lambda_3, ..., \lambda_n \right) = gA$$

$$= Ag = \mathrm{diag}\left(\begin{pmatrix} 0 & \lambda_2 \\ \lambda_1 & 0 \end{pmatrix}, \lambda_3, ..., \lambda_n \right),$$

which implies that $\lambda_1 = \lambda_2$. By a similar argument, any other pair of λ's must be equal. So g has the form $\mathrm{diag}(\lambda, ..., \lambda) = \lambda \cdot I$ for some $\lambda \in \mathbb{C}$ with unit norm. $\square$

Corollary 9.11.

(1) $SU(2)$ *is not isomorphic to* $SO(3)$.

(2) $SU(n) \times U(1)$ *is not isomorphic to* $U(n)$.

Proof. Their centers are not isomorphic. $\square$

Remember that $SU(2)$ and $SO(3)$ have isomorphic Lie algebras. There exists 2-to-1 homomorphism from $SU(2)$ to $SO(3)$ which is a local diffeomorphism. Corollary 9.11 (or the fact that they are not homeomorphic by Proposition 8.21) says that "2-to-1" cannot be improved to "1-to-1".

The pair $SU(n) \times U(1)$ and $U(n)$ are diffeomorphic, but the natural diffeomorphism between them does not preserve the group structure. They have isomorphic Lie algebras because there is an n-to-1 homomorphism from $SU(n) \times U(1)$ to $U(n)$ which is a local diffeomorphism. These statements are all justified in Exercise 4.21. The corollary implies that "n-to-1" cannot be improved to "1-to-1".

3. Conjugates of a maximal torus

The standard maximal tori are not the only maximal tori of $SO(n)$, $U(n)$, $Sp(n)$ and $SU(n)$. Other ones are obtained by conjugating the standard ones.

Proposition 9.12. *If T is a maximal torus of a matrix group G, then for any $g \in G$, $gTg^{-1} := \{gag^{-1} \mid a \in T\}$ is also a maximal torus of G.*

Proof. The conjugation map $C_g : G \to G$, which sends $a \to gag^{-1}$, is an isomorphism. So the image of T under C_g, namely gTg^{-1}, is isomorphic to T and is therefore a torus. If $\tilde{T} \subset G$ were a higher dimensional torus containing gTg^{-1}, then $C_g^{-1}(\tilde{T})$ would be a higher dimensional torus containing T. This is not possible, so gTg^{-1} must be maximal. $\square$

Since the standard maximal torus is not a normal subgroup, it differs from some of its conjugates. The main result of this section is that there are enough different conjugates to cover the whole group.

Theorem 9.13. *Let* $G \in \{SO(n), U(n), SU(n), Sp(n)\}$, *and let* T *be the standard maximal torus of* G. *Then every element of* G *is contained in* gTg^{-1} *for some* $g \in G$.

A more general fact is true, which we will not prove: the conjugates of any maximal torus of any path-connected compact matrix group cover the group.

Theorem 9.13 says that:

(9.1)   For each $x \in G$, there exists $g \in G$ such that $x \in gTg^{-1}$.

This is equivalent to:

(9.2)   For each $x \in G$, there exists $g \in G$ such that $gxg^{-1} \in T$.

In other words, every $x \in G$ can be conjugated into the diagonal or block-diagonal form that characterizes elements of the standard maximal torus.

In Equation 9.2, think of g as a change of basis matrix, as explained in Section 7 of Chapter 1. The linear transformation R_x is represented with respect to the orthonormal basis $\{e_1 g, ..., e_n g\}$ by the matrix $gxg^{-1} \in T$.

The example $G = SO(3)$ helps clarify this idea. Let $x \in SO(3)$. The theorem insures that there exists $g \in SO(3)$ such that

$$gxg^{-1} = \begin{pmatrix} \cos\theta & \sin\theta & 0 \\ -\sin\theta & \cos\theta & 0 \\ 0 & 0 & 1 \end{pmatrix}$$

for some $\theta \in [0, 2\pi)$. This is the matrix representing R_x in the basis $\{e_1g, e_2g, e_3g\}$, which means that R_x is a rotation through angle θ about the line spanned by e_3g. To verify this explicitly, notice:

$$(9.3) \qquad e_3(gxg^{-1}) = e_3 \Rightarrow (e_3g)x = e_3g,$$

$$e_1(gxg^{-1}) = (\cos\theta)e_1 + (\sin\theta)e_2 \Rightarrow (e_1g)x = (\cos\theta)e_1g + (\sin\theta)e_2g,$$

$$e_2(gxg^{-1}) = (\cos\theta)e_2 - (\sin\theta)e_1 \Rightarrow (e_2g)x = (\cos\theta)e_2g - (\sin\theta)e_1g.$$

We conclude that *every element of $SO(3)$ represents a rotation!*

Analogous interpretations hold for $SO(n)$. Take $SO(5)$ for example. An element, y, of the standard maximal torus of $SO(5)$ is particularly simple: R_y represents a rotation by some angle θ_1 in the plane span$\{e_1, e_2\}$ and a simultaneous rotation by a second angle θ_2 in the plane span$\{e_3, e_4\}$. The theorem says that every $x \in SO(5)$ is equally simple. There exist $g \in SO(5)$ such that R_x represents a simultaneous rotation in the planes span$\{e_1g, e_2g\}$ and span$\{e_3g, e_4g\}$. Notice that these two planes are orthogonal because $g \in SO(5)$. Similarly, every element of $SO(n)$ represents a simultaneous rotation in a collection of orthogonal planes.

Before proving Theorem 9.13, we review some linear algebra terminology. Let $\mathbb{K} \in \{\mathbb{R}, \mathbb{C}\}$, and let $f : \mathbb{K}^n \to \mathbb{K}^n$ be a linear transformation. Recall that $\lambda \in \mathbb{K}$ is called an <u>eigenvalue</u> of f if $f(v) = \lambda \cdot v$ for some non-zero $v \in \mathbb{K}^n$. Notice that for any $\lambda \in \mathbb{K}$,

$$\mathcal{V}(\lambda) := \{v \in \mathbb{K}^n \mid f(v) = \lambda \cdot v\}$$

is a subspace of $\mathbb{K}^n$ (this is false for $\mathbb{K} = \mathbb{H}$). Notice that λ is an eigenvalue of f exactly when $\mathcal{V}(\lambda)$ has dimension ≥ 1. The non-zero vectors in $\mathcal{V}(\lambda)$ are called <u>eigenvectors</u> associated to λ. For a matrix $A \in M_n(\mathbb{K})$, a basic fact from linear algebra is: $\lambda \in \mathbb{K}$ is an eigenvalue of R_A if and only if $\det(A - \lambda \cdot I) = 0$.

Lemma 9.14. *Any linear transformation $f : \mathbb{C}^n \to \mathbb{C}^n$ has an eigenvalue.*

Proof. $f = R_A$ for some $A \in M_n(\mathbb{C})$. The fundamental theorem of algebra says that every polynomial of degree ≥ 1 with coefficients in $\mathbb{C}$ has a root in $\mathbb{C}$. In particular,

$$g(\lambda) := \det(A - \lambda \cdot I)$$

equals zero for some $\lambda \in \mathbb{C}$, which is an eigenvalue of f. $\qquad\square$

Proposition 9.15. *For every $A \in U(n)$, R_A has an orthonormal basis of eigenvectors.*

Proof. Let $A \in U(n)$. By Lemma 9.14, there exists an eigenvalue λ_1 of R_A. Let $v_1 \in \mathbb{C}^n$ be an associated eigenvector, which can be chosen to have norm 1, since any multiple of an eigenvector is an eigenvector. Notice that $\lambda_1 \neq 0$, since R_A is invertible.

To find a second eigenvector, we use that A is unitary. The key observation is: if $w \in \mathbb{C}^n$ is orthogonal to v_1 (in the hermitian inner product), then $R_A(w)$ is also orthogonal to v_1. To justify this, notice that:

$$(9.4) \quad \langle wA, v_1 \rangle = \langle w, v_1 A^{-1} \rangle = \left\langle w, \frac{1}{\lambda_1} v_1 \right\rangle = \langle w, v_1 \rangle (1/\overline{\lambda}_1) = 0.$$

This means that $R_A : \mathbb{C}^n \to \mathbb{C}^n$ restricts to a linear transformation,

$$R_A : \mathrm{span}\{v_1\}^\perp \to \mathrm{span}\{v_1\}^\perp,$$

where

$$\mathrm{span}\{v_1\}^\perp := \{w \in \mathbb{C}^n \mid w \text{ is orthogonal to } v_1\},$$

which is an $(n-1)$ dimensional $\mathbb{C}$-subspace of $\mathbb{C}^n$. By applying Lemma 9.14 a second time, the restricted R_A has a unit-length eigenvector $v_2 \in \mathrm{span}\{v_1\}^\perp$, and R_A restricts further to a linear transformation

$$R_A : \mathrm{span}\{v_1, v_2\}^\perp \to \mathrm{span}\{v_1, v_2\}^\perp.$$

Repeating this argument a total of n times proves the lemma. $\qquad\square$

As a corollary of Proposition 9.15, we prove that Theorem 9.13 is true when $G = U(n)$.

Corollary 9.16. *For any $A \in U(n)$, there exists $g \in U(n)$ such that gAg^{-1} is diagonal and hence lies in the standard maximal torus of $U(n)$.*

Proof. Let $\{v_1, ..., v_n\}$ be an orthonormal basis of eigenvectors of R_A with eigenvalues $\{\lambda_1, ..., \lambda_n\}$. Let g denote the matrix whose i^{th} row equals v_i, so that $e_i g = v_i$, for each $i = 1, ..., n$. Notice that $g \in U(n)$. We claim that

$$gAg^{-1} = \text{diag}(\lambda_1, ..., \lambda_n).$$

This is simply because gAg^{-1} represents the linear transformation R_A in the basis $\{v_1, ..., v_n\}$. To understand this more concretely, notice that for each $i = 1, ..., n$,

$$e_i(gAg^{-1}) = v_i Ag^{-1} = \lambda_i v_i g^{-1} = \lambda_i e_i.$$

$\square$

Next we verify Theorem 9.13 when $G = SU(n)$.

Corollary 9.17. *For any $A \in SU(n)$, there exists $g \in SU(n)$ such that gAg^{-1} is diagonal and hence lies in the standard maximal torus of $SU(n)$.*

Proof. Let $A \in SU(n)$. By the previous corollary, there exists some $g \in U(n)$ such that gAg^{-1} is diagonal. Notice that for any $\theta \in [0, 2\pi)$,

$$(e^{i\theta}g)A(e^{i\theta}g)^{-1} = gAg^{-1}.$$

Further, θ can easily be chosen such that $e^{i\theta}g \in SU(n)$. $\square$

The $U(n)$ case also helps us prove the $Sp(n)$ case:

Corollary 9.18. *For any $A \in Sp(n)$, there exists $g \in Sp(n)$ such that gAg^{-1} is diagonal with all entries in $\mathbb{C}$ and hence lies in the standard maximal torus of $Sp(n)$.*

Proof. Let $A \in Sp(n)$. Recall from Chapter 2 that the injective homomorphism $\Psi_n : Sp(n) \to U(2n)$ is defined such that the following diagram commutes:

$$
\begin{array}{ccc}
\mathbb{H}^n & \xrightarrow{g_n} & \mathbb{C}^{2n} \\
R_A \downarrow & & \downarrow R_{\Psi_n(A)} \\
\mathbb{H}^n & \xrightarrow{g_n} & \mathbb{C}^{2n}
\end{array}
$$

Since every unitary matrix has a unit-length eigenvector, there exists $u_1 \in \mathbb{C}^{2n}$ such that $R_{\Psi_n(A)}(u_1) = \lambda_1 u_1$ for some $\lambda_1 \in \mathbb{C}$ with $|\lambda_1| = 1$. Let $v_1 := g_n^{-1}(u_1) \in \mathbb{H}^n$. We claim that $R_A(v_1) = \lambda_1 v_1$. This is because:

$$g_n(\lambda_1 v_1) = \lambda_1 g_n(v_1) = \lambda_1 u_1 = R_{\Psi_n(A)}(u_1) = g_n(R_A(v_1)).$$

Next notice that if $w \in \mathbb{H}^n$ is orthogonal to v_1 (with respect to the symplectic inner product), then so is $R_A(w)$. The verification is identical to Equation 9.4. So $R_A : \mathbb{H}^n \to \mathbb{H}^n$ restricts to an $\mathbb{H}$-linear function from the following $(n-1)$-dimensional $\mathbb{H}$-subspace of $\mathbb{H}^n$ to itself:

$$\mathrm{span}\{v_1\}^\perp = \{w \in \mathbb{H}^n \mid w \text{ is orthogonal to } v_1\}.$$

Therefore, $R_{\Psi_n(A)} : \mathbb{C}^{2n} \to \mathbb{C}^{2n}$ restricts to a linear function from $g_n(\mathrm{span}\{v_1\}^\perp)$ to itself. Let $u_2 \in \mathbb{C}^{2n}$ be a unit-length eigenvector of this restriction of $R_{\Psi_n(A)}$, with eigenvalue λ_2, and let $v_2 := g_n^{-1}(u_2)$. As before, $R_A(v_2) = \lambda_2 v_2$. Repeating this argument a total of n times produces an orthonormal basis $\{v_1, ..., v_n\}$ of $\mathbb{H}^n$ and unit-length complex numbers $\{\lambda_1, ..., \lambda_n\}$ such that $R_A(v_i) = \lambda_i v_i$ for each i.

Finally, if $g \in Sp(n)$ is the matrix whose rows are $v_1, ..., v_n$, then

$$gAg^{-1} = \mathrm{diag}(\lambda_1, ..., \lambda_n),$$

exactly as in the proof of Corollary 9.16. $\qquad\qquad\qquad\qquad\square$

Finally, we prove Theorem 9.13 in the case $G = SO(n)$.

Proposition 9.19. *For any $A \in SO(n)$, there exists $g \in SO(n)$ such that gAg^{-1} lies in the standard maximal torus of $SO(n)$.*

Proof. Let $A \in SO(n)$. We can regard A as an n by n complex matrix whose entries happen to all be real numbers. Regarded as such, $A \in SU(n)$, so there exists $v \in \mathbb{C}^n$ such that $vA = \lambda v$ for some unit-length $\lambda \in \mathbb{C}$. Let $\overline{v} \in \mathbb{C}^n$ denote the result of conjugating all of the entries of v. Notice that:

$$(9.5) \qquad\qquad \overline{v}A = \overline{v}\overline{A} = \overline{vA} = \overline{\lambda v} = \overline{\lambda}\overline{v},$$

so $\overline{v}$ is also an eigenvector of R_A, with eigenvalue $\overline{\lambda}$.

CASE 1: Suppose $\lambda \in \mathbb{R}$ (so $\lambda = \overline{\lambda} = \pm 1$). In this case, Equation 9.5 says that $\overline{v}$ is also an eigenvector associated to λ. The vector

$$Z := \frac{v + \overline{v}}{|v + \overline{v}|}$$

has all real entries, so $Z \in \mathbb{R}^n$. Further, $ZA = \lambda Z$, since sums of eigenvectors are eigenvectors.

CASE 2: Suppose $\lambda \notin \mathbb{R}$. Write $\lambda = e^{i\theta}$ for some angle θ, which is not an integer multiple of π. Define:

$$X = v + \overline{v},$$

$$Y = \mathbf{i}(v - \overline{v}).$$

All entries of X and Y are real, so $X, Y \in \mathbb{R}^n$. It is straightforward to check that X and Y are orthogonal. Observe that:

$$
\begin{aligned}
(9.6) \qquad XA &= (v + \overline{v})A = e^{i\theta}v + e^{-i\theta}\overline{v} \\
&= (\cos\theta + \mathbf{i}\sin\theta)v + (\cos\theta - \mathbf{i}\sin\theta)\overline{v} \\
&= (\cos\theta)(v + \overline{v}) + (\sin\theta)(\mathbf{i}v - \mathbf{i}\overline{v}) \\
&= (\cos\theta)X + (\sin\theta)Y.
\end{aligned}
$$

Similarly, $YA = (-\sin\theta)X + (\cos\theta)Y.$

Using the fact that θ is not a multiple of π, Equation 9.6 implies that X and Y have the same norm, which is non-zero since $v \neq 0$. So R_A rotates span$\{X, Y\} \subset \mathbb{R}^n$ by an angle θ. If X and Y are re-scaled to have unit-length, they still satisfy the punchline of Equation 9.6:

$$XA = (\cos\theta)X + (\sin\theta)Y,$$

$$YA = (-\sin\theta)X + (\cos\theta)Y.$$

In case 1, let $\Omega = \text{span}(Z) \subset \mathbb{R}^n$. In case 2, let

$$\Omega = \text{span}(X, Y) \subset \mathbb{R}^n.$$

In either case, Ω is stable under $R_A : \mathbb{R}^n \to \mathbb{R}^n$, meaning that $R_A(w) \in \Omega$ for all $w \in \Omega$. By an argument analogous to Equation 9.4, the subspace

$$\Omega^{\perp} = \{w \in \mathbb{R}^n \mid w \text{ is orthogonal to every element of } \Omega\}$$

is also stable under R_A. So we can repeat the above argument on the restriction of R_A to $\Omega^{\perp}$.

Repeating this argument enough times produces an orthonormal basis of $\mathbb{R}^n$ of the form $\{X_1, Y_1, ..., X_k, Y_k, Z_1, ..., Z_l\}$, with $2k + l = n$. If g is the matrix whose rows equal these basis vectors, then

$$gAg^{-1} = \text{diag}(\mathcal{R}_{\theta_1}, ..., \mathcal{R}_{\theta_k}, \lambda_1, ..., \lambda_l),$$

where each λ is ± 1. By re-ordering the basis, we can assume that the negative lambda's come first. There are an even number of negative lambda's because $\det(gAg^{-1}) = \det(A) = 1$. Each pair of negative lambda's is a rotation block, since $\mathrm{diag}(-1,-1) = \mathcal{R}_\pi$. It follows that gAg^{-1} lies in the standard maximal torus T of $SO(n)$.

Since the basis is orthonormal, $g \in O(n)$. If $g \in SO(n)$, then we are done, so assume that $g \in O(n) - SO(n)$. In this case, define:

$$a := \mathrm{diag}\left(\begin{pmatrix} 0 & 1 \\ 1 & 0 \end{pmatrix}, 1, ..., 1 \right) \in O(n) - SO(n).$$

Notice that $ag \in SO(n)$ and that $aTa^{-1} = T$, so,

$$(ag)A(ag)^{-1} = a(gAg^{-1})a^{-1} \in T,$$

which verifies that $ag \in SO(n)$ conjugates A into T. $\square$

This completes our proof of Theorem 9.13.

4. The Lie algebra of a maximal torus

In this section, let $G \in \{SO(n), U(n), SU(n), Sp(n)\}$ and let $\mathfrak{g}$ be the Lie algebra of G. Let $T = T(G) \subset G$ be the standard maximal torus of G, and let $\tau = \tau(\mathfrak{g}) \subset \mathfrak{g}$ be the Lie algebra of T. It is straightforward to calculate:

$$\tau(so(2m)) = \left\{ \mathrm{diag}\left(\begin{pmatrix} 0 & \theta_1 \\ -\theta_1 & 0 \end{pmatrix}, ..., \begin{pmatrix} 0 & \theta_m \\ -\theta_m & 0 \end{pmatrix} \right) \mid \theta_i \in \mathbb{R} \right\},$$

$$\tau(so(2m+1)) = \left\{ \mathrm{diag}\left(\begin{pmatrix} 0 & \theta_1 \\ -\theta_1 & 0 \end{pmatrix}, ..., \begin{pmatrix} 0 & \theta_m \\ -\theta_m & 0 \end{pmatrix}, 0 \right) \mid \theta_i \in \mathbb{R} \right\},$$

(9.7)
$$\tau(u(n)) = \{\mathrm{diag}(i\theta_1, ..., i\theta_n) \mid \theta_i \in \mathbb{R}\},$$
$$\tau(sp(n)) = \{\mathrm{diag}(i\theta_1, ..., i\theta_n) \mid \theta_i \in \mathbb{R}\},$$
$$\tau(su(n)) = \{\mathrm{diag}(i\theta_1, ..., i\theta_{n-1}, -i(\theta_1 + \cdots + \theta_{n-1})) \mid \theta_i \in \mathbb{R}\}.$$

Compare to Theorem 9.8, where we described $T(G)$ using the same parameters θ_i that are used above to describe $\tau(\mathfrak{g})$. The descriptions correspond via matrix exponentiation. The exponential image of a vector in $\tau(\mathfrak{g})$ equals the element of $T(G)$ described by the same angles. In $U(n)$ for example,

$$e^{\mathrm{diag}(i\theta_1, ..., i\theta_n)} = \mathrm{diag}(e^{i\theta_1}, ..., e^{i\theta_n}) \in T(U(n)).$$

Since T is abelian, its Lie algebra, τ, is abelian, which means that the Lie bracket of any pair of matrices in τ equals zero.

Using the fact that all elements of G can be conjugated into T, we will show that all elements of $\mathfrak{g}$ can be conjugated into τ.

Proposition 9.20. *For each $X \in \mathfrak{g}$ there exists $g \in G$ such that $Ad_g(X) \in \tau$.*

Proof. Choose $r > 0$ such that $\exp : \mathfrak{g} \to G$ is a diffeomorphism on the ball in $\mathfrak{g}$ of radius r centered at the origin. It will suffice to prove the proposition for $X \in \mathfrak{g}$ with $|X| < r$. By Theorem 9.13, there exists $g \in G$ such that $a := g(e^X)g^{-1} \in T$, so:

$$e^{\mathrm{Ad}_g(X)} = e^{gXg^{-1}} = g(e^X)g^{-1} = a \in T.$$

Remember that $|\mathrm{Ad}_g(X)| = |X| < r$, so $\mathrm{Ad}_g(X)$ is the unique vector with length $< r$ that exponentiates to $a \in T$. Equation 9.7 explicitly describes this vector in terms of the angles θ_i of a; in particular it lies in τ. $\qquad\square$

Proposition 9.20 is important in linear algebra. It says that any skew-symmetric or skew-hermitian or skew-symplectic matrix can be conjugated into the diagonal or block-diagonal form of Equation 9.7. This adds to the list in Theorem 9.13 of matrix types which can be conjugated into simple forms. In fact, Theorem 9.13 and Proposition 9.20 together give a beautifully uniform way of understanding many conjugation theorems from linear algebra!

A key application of Theorem 9.13 is the following proposition, which implies in particular that G is path-connected:

Proposition 9.21. *The exponential map $\exp : \mathfrak{g} \to G$ is surjective.*

Proof. We have an explicit description of the restriction $\exp : \tau \to T$, which is clearly surjective. For any $g \in G$, gTg^{-1} is a maximal torus with Lie algebra $Ad_g(\tau)$. Also, the restriction $\exp : \mathrm{Ad}_g(\tau) \to gTg^{-1}$ is surjective, since $e^{\mathrm{Ad}_g(X)} = ge^Xg^{-1}$ for all $X \in \tau$. Theorem 9.13 says that these conjugates cover G. $\qquad\square$

5. The shape of $SO(3)$

We saw in Section 6 of Chapter 8 that $SO(3)$ is diffeomorphic to $\mathbb{RP}^3$. We will now give a different proof, which relies on explicitly understanding the exponential map $\exp : so(3) \to SO(3)$.

Recall from Section 3 of Chapter 8 the following vector space isomorphism $f : \mathbb{R}^3 \to so(3)$:

$$(a, b, c) \overset{f}{\mapsto} \begin{pmatrix} 0 & -c & b \\ c & 0 & -a \\ -b & a & 0 \end{pmatrix}.$$

Recall that under this identification, $\mathrm{Ad}_g : so(3) \to so(3)$ corresponds to $L_g : \mathbb{R}^3 \to \mathbb{R}^3$ for all $g \in SO(3)$. More precisely,

$$(9.8) \qquad\qquad \mathrm{Ad}_g(f(a, b, c)) = f(g \cdot (a, b, c)).$$

Proposition 9.22. *For any* $A \in so(3)$, $L_{(e^A)} : \mathbb{R}^3 \to \mathbb{R}^3$ *is a right-handed rotation through angle* $|A|/\sqrt{2}$ *about the axis spanned by* $f^{-1}(A)$.

"Right-handed" means the rotation is in the direction that the fingers of your right hand curl when your thumb is pointed towards $f^{-1}(A)$.

Proof. Let $A \in so(3)$. By Proposition 9.20, there exists $g \in SO(3)$ such that

$$A = g \begin{pmatrix} 0 & -\theta & 0 \\ \theta & 0 & 0 \\ 0 & 0 & 0 \end{pmatrix} g^{-1}$$

for some $\theta \in \mathbb{R}$. Notice that $|A| = \sqrt{2}\theta$, so $\theta = |A|/\sqrt{2}$. Next,

$$\exp(A) = g \exp \begin{pmatrix} 0 & -\theta & 0 \\ \theta & 0 & 0 \\ 0 & 0 & 0 \end{pmatrix} g^{-1} = g \begin{pmatrix} \cos\theta & -\sin\theta & 0 \\ \sin\theta & \cos\theta & 0 \\ 0 & 0 & 1 \end{pmatrix} g^{-1}.$$

It follows that $L_{(e^A)}$ is a right-handed rotation through angle θ about the line spanned by $g \cdot (0, 0, 1)$. The verification is similar to Equation 9.3.

Finally, notice that by Equation 9.8, the rotation axis is:

$$g \cdot (0,0,1) = f^{-1} \left(\mathrm{Ad}_g \begin{pmatrix} 0 & -1 & 0 \\ 1 & 0 & 0 \\ 0 & 0 & 0 \end{pmatrix} \right) = \frac{1}{\theta} f^{-1}(A).$$

$\square$

Corollary 9.23. *Let $B = \{A \in so(3) \mid |A| \leq \pi\sqrt{2}\}$. The restriction $\exp : B \to SO(3)$ is surjective. It is not injective, but for $A_1, A_2 \in B$, $\exp(A_1) = \exp(A_2)$ if and only if $A_1 = -A_2$ and $|A_1| = |A_2| = \pi\sqrt{2}$.*

Proof. The image $\exp(B)$ contains matrices representing all right-handed rotations about all vectors in $\mathbb{R}^3$ through all angles $\theta \in [0, \pi]$. Notice that the right-handed rotation through angle θ about $A \in \mathbb{R}^3$ equals the right-handed rotation through angle $-\theta$ about $-A$. This is why $\exp(A) = \exp(-A)$ when $|A| = \pi\sqrt{2}$. $\square$

Points of $SO(3)$ are in one-to-one correspondence with points of $B/\sim$, where $\sim$ is the equivalence relationship on B that identified each point on the boundary of B with its antipode (its negative).

What does this have to do with $\mathbb{RP}^3$? Well, B is homeomorphic to the "upper-hemisphere" V of S^3:

$$V := \{(x_0, x_1, x_2, x_3) \in S^3 \subset \mathbb{R}^4 \mid x_0 \geq 0\},$$

by an argument analogous to the proof of Proposition 7.15. A typical line through the origin in $\mathbb{R}^4$ intersects V in exactly one point. The only exceptions are the lines in the subspace $\{x_0 = 0\}$; these intersect V in a pair of antipodal points on its boundary. So $\mathbb{RP}^3$ can be modelled as the upper hemisphere V modulo identification of antipodal boundary pairs. This is another way of understanding why $SO(3)$ is diffeomorphic to $\mathbb{RP}^3$.

6. The rank of a compact matrix group

Let $G \in \{SO(n), U(n), SU(n), Sp(n)\}$. Let T be the standard maximal torus of G. In this section we prove the following:

Theorem 9.24. *Every maximal torus of G equals gTg^{-1} for some $g \in G$.*

Our proof actually holds when T is any maximal torus of any path-connected compact matrix group, granting the previously mentioned fact that the conjugates of T cover G in this generality.

In particular, any two maximal tori of G have the same dimension, so the following is well-defined:

Definition 9.25. *The <u>rank</u> of G is the dimension of a maximal torus.*

The ranks of our familiar compact groups are:

$$\text{rank}(SO(2n)) = \text{rank}(SO(2n+1)) = \text{rank}(U(n))$$
$$= \text{rank}(Sp(n)) = \text{rank}(SU(n+1)) = n.$$

Isomorphic groups clearly have the same rank, so rank is a useful invariant for proving that two groups are not isomorphic. The proof of Theorem 9.24 relies on a useful fact about tori:

Lemma 9.26. *For any n, there exists a $\in T^n$ such that the set $\{a, a^2, a^3, a^4, ...\}$ is dense in T^n.*

Proof of the $n = 1$ case. Let θ be an irrational angle, which means an irrational multiple of π. Let $a := (e^{i\theta}) \in T^1 = U(1)$. To verify that this choice works, notice that $\{a = (e^{i\theta}), a^2 = (e^{2i\theta}), a^3 = (e^{3i\theta}), ...\}$ is an infinite sequence of points which are all *distinct* because θ is irrational. Since $U(1)$ is compact, some subsequence converges (Proposition 4.24). This convergent subsequence must be Cauchy, which means that for any $\epsilon > 0$, we can find integers $n_1 < n_2$ such that $\text{dist}(a^{n_1}, a^{n_2}) < \epsilon$. Next, notice that for any integer m,

$$\text{dist}(a^{m+(n_2-n_1)}, a^m) = \text{dist}(a^m a^{n_2} a^{-n_1}, a^m)$$
$$= \text{dist}(a^{n_2} a^{-n_1}, I) = \text{dist}(a^{n_2}, a^{n_1}) < \epsilon.$$

So the sequence $\{a^{(n_2-n_1)}, a^{2(n_2-n_1)}, a^{3(n_2-n_1)}, ...\}$ takes baby steps of uniform size $< \epsilon$ and thus comes within a distance ϵ of every element of $U(1)$ as it marches around the circle. Since $\epsilon > 0$ was arbitrary, the lemma follows. $\square$

For $n > 1$, we must choose $a := (e^{i\theta_1}, ..., e^{i\theta_n}) \in T^n$ such that the θ's are *rationally independent*, which means there are no equalities of the form $\sum_{k=1}^{n} s_k \theta_k = \pi$, where s_k are rational numbers. The proof that this works is found in [**2**, page 66]. An alternative purely topological proof of Lemma 9.26 is found in [**1**].

Proof of Theorem 9.24. Let $T' \subset G$ be a maximal torus. Choose $a \in T'$ such that $\{a, a^2, a^3, ...\}$ is dense in T'. Choose $g \in G$ such that $gag^{-1} \in T$. Since T is a subgroup, $(gag^{-1})^n = ga^n g^{-1} \in T$ for every integer n, so a dense subset of $gT'g^{-1}$ lies in T. Since T is closed, $gT'g^{-1} \subset T$. Since $gT'g^{-1}$ is a *maximal* torus, $gT'g^{-1} = T$. $\quad\square$

7. Who commutes with whom?

Let $G \in \{SO(n), U(n), SU(n), Sp(n)\}$. In order to better understand the group structure of G, we wish for each $x \in G$ to describe the set of elements of G that commute with x. We first solve this problem when $x \in T = $ the standard maximal torus of G. For a "regular" $x \in T$, we will show that x commutes only with the other elements of T. Remember that in Theorem 9.8, an element of T is described by a list of angles $\theta_1, ..., \theta_m$.

Definition 9.27. *An element $x \in T$ is called <u>regular</u> if its angles are all distinct, and in the case $G = SO(n)$, none are equal to 0 or π.*

When $G = SU(n)$, an element of T looks like
$$\text{diag}(e^{i\theta_1}, ..., e^{i\theta_{n-1}}, e^{-i(\theta_1 + \cdots + \theta_{n-1})}),$$
and the "distinct angle" restriction in the definition includes the final summed angle.

The identity $I \in T$ is as non-regular as possible. Also, if $-I \in G$ (as is the case for $G = SO(2m)$ but not $G = SO(2m + 1)$), then $-I \in T$ and is very non-regular. Notice that I and $-I$ commute with every element of G and are contained in every maximal torus of G.

Proposition 9.28. *If $x \in T$ is regular, then x only commutes with other elements of T, so T is the only maximal torus that contains x.*

Proof. In the proof of Theorem 9.8, we verified that T is maximal by showing that if $g \in G$ commutes with all of T, then $g \in T$. We leave it to the reader in Exercise 9.2 to modify this argument, obtaining the slightly stronger claim that if $g \in G$ commutes with a single regular $x \in T$, then $g \in T$. $\quad\square$

Next, we show that the problem of determining who commutes with $x \in G$ reduces to the case $x \in T$.

Definition 9.29. *An element $y \in G$ is called* <u>*regular*</u> *if $y = gxg^{-1}$ for some $g \in G$ and some regular $x \in T$.*

For example, an element $y \in U(n)$ is regular if and only if its eigenvalues all have multiplicity 1, which means that the vector space of eigenvectors associated to any eigenvalue is 1 (complex) dimensional.

Corollary 9.30. *A regular element of G is contained in only one maximal torus and commutes only with elements of that maximal torus.*

Proof. Let $y \in G$ be regular, which means $y = gxg^{-1}$ for some $g \in G$ and some regular $x \in T$. We claim that y commutes only with elements of the maximal torus gTg^{-1}. This follows from the previous proposition, since $z \in G$ commutes with x if and only if gzg^{-1} commutes with y. $\qquad\square$

It is also straightforward to determine which elements of G commute with a non-regular $x \in T$ and hence with a non-regular $x \in G$. In summary, basic facts about maximal tori empower us to completely answer the question: who commutes with whom in G?

8. The classification of compact matrix groups

A major achievement of Lie group theory is the classification of compact matrix groups. The only such groups we have encountered so far are $SO(n)$, $O(n)$, $U(n)$, $SU(n)$, $Sp(n)$, and products of these, like for example $SO(3) \times SO(5) \times SU(2)$. It turns out that there are not many more than these.

Theorem 9.31. *The Lie algebra of every compact matrix group is isomorphic to the Lie algebra of a product $G_1 \times G_2 \times \cdots \times G_k$, where each G_i is one of $\{SO(n), SU(n), Sp(n)\}$ for some n, or is one of a list of five possible exceptions.*

The five "exceptional matrix groups" mentioned in the theorem are named:

(1) G_2, which has dimension 14;

(2) F_4, which has dimension 52;

(3) E_6, which has dimension 78;

(4) E_7, which has dimension 133;

(5) E_8, which has dimension 248.

It is beyond the scope of this text to construct the exceptional groups or to address the proof of Theorem 9.31.

We have seen that non-isomorphic matrix groups sometimes have isomorphic Lie algebras. For example, $U(n)$ is not on the list in Theorem 9.31 because it has the same Lie algebra as $SU(n) \times SO(2)$, by Exercise 4.21.

The problem of determining all matrix groups with the same Lie algebra as $G_1 \times G_2 \times \cdots \times G_k$ is well-understood, but is also beyond the scope of this text. Aside from this detail, the theorem gives a complete classification of compact matrix groups!

9. Lie groups

Lie groups have proven to be among the most fundamental objects in mathematics.

Definition 9.32. *A Lie group is a manifold, G, with a smooth group operation $G \times G \to G$.*

In other words, a Lie group is a manifold which is also a group. One often adds to the definition that the "inverse map" $G \to G$, sending $g \mapsto g^{-1}$, is smooth; however, this turns out to be a consequence of the smoothness of the group operation $(g_1, g_2) \mapsto g_1 \cdot g_2$.

In Chapter 7, we proved that matrix groups are manifolds. It is straightforward to see that the group operation is smooth and therefore that matrix groups are Lie groups.

Not all Lie groups are matrix groups, but at least it has been shown that:

Theorem 9.33. *Every compact Lie group is smoothly isomorphic to a matrix group.*

All important structures of matrix groups carry over to Lie groups. For example, the Lie algebra $\mathfrak{g}$ of a Lie group G is defined as you would expect:

$$\mathfrak{g} = T_I G.$$

For every $g \in G$, the conjugation map $C_g : G \to G$ sending $x \mapsto gxg^{-1}$ is smooth, so one can define:

$$Ad_g := d(C_g)_I : \mathfrak{g} \to \mathfrak{g}.$$

Next, the Lie bracket operation in $\mathfrak{g}$ is defined as you would expect: for $A, B \in \mathfrak{g}$,

$$[A, B] := \frac{d}{dt}\Big|_{t=0} \mathrm{Ad}_{a(t)} B,$$

where $a(t)$ is any differentiable path in G with $a(0) = I$ and with $a'(0) = A$. It turns out that this operation satisfies the familiar Lie bracket properties of Proposition 8.4. Next, the exponential map $\exp : \mathfrak{g} \to G$ is defined with inspiration from Proposition 6.10: For $A \in \mathfrak{g}$, the path $t \mapsto e^{tA}$ means the integral curve of the vector field on G whose value at $g \in G$ is $d(\mathcal{L}_g)_I(A) \in T_g G$, where $\mathcal{L}_g : G \to G$ denotes the map $x \mapsto g \cdot x$.

Further evidence that Lie groups are only slightly more general than matrix groups is provided by the following non-trivial theorem:

Theorem 9.34. *The Lie algebra of any Lie group is isomorphic to the Lie algebra of a matrix group.*

For readers with more advanced topology background, we mention that every *simply connected* Lie group is smoothly isomorphic to a matrix group.

10. Exercises

Ex. 9.1. In Theorem 9.10, prove the remaining cases $G = SU(n)$, $G = SO(n)$, $G = Sp(n)$.

Ex. 9.2. Prove Proposition 9.28.

Ex. 9.3. Prove that the standard maximal torus of $SO(3)$ is also a maximal torus of $GL_3(\mathbb{R})$. Do its conjugates cover $GL_3(\mathbb{R})$?

Ex. 9.4. If $T_1 \subset G_1$ and $T_2 \subset G_2$ are maximal tori of matrix groups G_1 and G_2, prove that $T_1 \times T_2$ is a maximal torus of $G_1 \times G_2$.

Ex. 9.5. Prove $U(n)/Z(U(n))$ is isomorphic to $SU(n)/Z(SU(n))$.

Ex. 9.6. Let $G \in \{SO(n), U(n), SU(n), Sp(n)\}$, and let $\mathfrak{g}$ denote its Lie algebra. Characterize the elements $X \in \mathfrak{g}$ that are <u>regular</u>, meaning that X is tangent to only one maximal torus and commutes only with other vectors that are tangent to that maximal torus.

Ex. 9.7. Use maximal tori to find a simple proof that if $A \in U(n)$, then

$$\det(e^A) = e^{\text{trace}(A)}.$$

This is a special case of Lemma 6.15.

Ex. 9.8. Let $A = \text{diag}(1, 1, ..., 1, -1) \in O(n)$. An element of $O(n)$ of the form gAg^{-1} for $g \in O(n)$ is called a <u>reflection</u>.

(1) Show that $R_A : \mathbb{R}^n \to \mathbb{R}^n$ fixes $\text{span}\{e_1, ..., e_{n-1}\}$ and can be visualized as a reflection across this subspace.

(2) Show $R_{gAg^{-1}} : \mathbb{R}^n \to \mathbb{R}^n$ fixes $\text{span}\{e_1 g^{-1}, ..., e_{n-1} g^{-1}\}$ and can be visualized as a reflection across this subspace.

(3) Prove that every element of $O(2) - SO(2)$ is a reflection, and every element of $SO(2)$ is the product of two reflections.

(4) Prove that every element of the standard maximal torus of $SO(n)$ is the product of finitely many reflections.

(5) Prove that every element of $O(n)$ is the product of finitely many reflections.

Ex. 9.9. Identify $Sp(1)$ with the unit-length quaternions $S^3 \subset \mathbb{H}$.

(1) Prove that the conjugates of the standard maximal torus of $Sp(1)$ are exactly the intersections of S^3 with the 2-dimensional $\mathbb{R}$-subspaces of $\mathbb{H}$ that contain 1.

(2) Prove that two elements $a_1 + b_1\mathbf{i} + c_1\mathbf{j} + d_1\mathbf{k}$, $a_2 + b_2\mathbf{i} + c_2\mathbf{j} + d_2\mathbf{k}$ in $Sp(1)$ are conjugate if and only if $a_1 = a_2$.

(3) Prove that two elements of $SU(2)$ are conjugate if and only if they have the same trace.
Hint: Consider the isomorphism $\Psi_1 : Sp(1) \to SU(2)$.

Ex. 9.10. If $H \subset G$ is a subgroup, define the <u>normalizer</u> of H as $N(H) := \{g \in G \mid gHg^{-1} = H\}$. Prove that $N(H)$ is a subgroup of G and that H is a normal subgroup of $N(H)$.

Ex. 9.11. Let $G \in \{SO(n), U(n), SU(n), Sp(n)\}$, let T be the standard maximal torus of G, and let $\tau \subset \mathfrak{g}$ denote their Lie algebras.

(1) Prove that if $X \in \mathfrak{g}$ commutes with every vector in τ, then $X \in \tau$. In other words, τ is a "maximal abelian" subspace.

(2) Prove that the Lie algebra of $N(T)$ equals τ.
Hint: Use part (1) and also Exercise 8.13.

(3) Conclude that $N(T)$ is comprised of finitely many nonintersecting subsets of G, each diffeomorphic to T.

Ex. 9.12. Prove that the normalizer of the standard maximal torus T of $Sp(1)$ is:
$$N(T) = T \cup (T \cdot \mathbf{j}).$$

Ex. 9.13. Prove that the normalizer of the standard maximal torus T of $SO(3)$ is:
$$N(T) = T \cup \left\{ \begin{pmatrix} \cos\theta & \sin\theta & 0 \\ \sin\theta & -\cos\theta & 0 \\ 0 & 0 & -1 \end{pmatrix} \middle| \theta \in [0, 2\pi) \right\}.$$

Bibliography

1. A. Baker, *Matrix Groups: an Introduction to Lie Group Theory*, Springer, 2002.

2. Cornfed, Formin, Sinai, *Ergotic Theory*, Springer-Verlag, 1982.

3. M. Curtis, *Matrix Groups, Second Edition*, Springer, 1975, 1984.

4. Frobenius, Journal für die Reine und Angewandte Mathematik, 1878, Vol. 84, 1-63.

5. J. Gallian, *Contemporary Abstract Algebra*, 2002, Houghton Mifflin Co.

6. F. Goodman, *Algebra: Abstract and Concrete Stressing Symmetry*, Prentice Hall, 2003.

7. B. Hall, *Lie Groups, Lie Algebras, and Representations*, Springer, 2003.

8. F.R. Harvey, *Spinors and Calibrations*, Perspectives in Mathematics, Vol. 9, 1990.

9. S. Helgason, *Differential Geometry, Lie Groups, and Symmetric Spaces*, American Math Society, 2001.

10. R. Howe, *Very basic Lie theory*, American Mathematical Monthly, **90** (1983), 600-623; Correction, Amer. Math. Monthly **91** (1984), 247.

11. W. Rossmann, *Lie Groups: an Introduction Through Linear Groups*, Oxford Science Publications, 2002.

12. M. Spivak, *A Comprehensive Introduction to Differential Geometry, Volume 1*, 1979.

13. F. Warner, *Foundations of Differentiable Manifolds and Lie Groups*, Springer-Verlag, 1983.

14. J. Weeks, *The Poincaré dodecahedral space and the mystery of the missing fluctuations*, Notices of the AMS **51** (2004), number 6, 610-619.

Index

Titles in This Series

TITLES IN THIS SERIES